Ist Grade

Hooked on Phonics®

Spelling

Chapter I

b or d?

Write a "b" or "d" to complete each word.

Draw lines to match each word to a picture.

__ag	__rum	__at

__ee	__ot	__oor

Hooked on First Grade *Spelling Super Workbook*

c or k?

Write a "c" or "k" to complete each word.

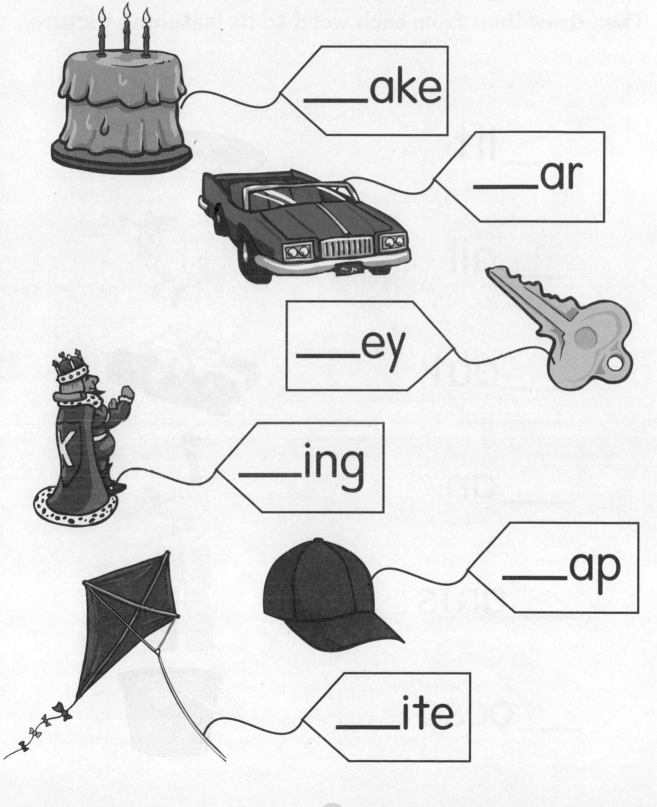

___ake

___ar

___ey

___ing

___ap

___ite

3

g or p?

Write a "g" or "p" to complete each word.
Then draw lines from each word to its matching picture.

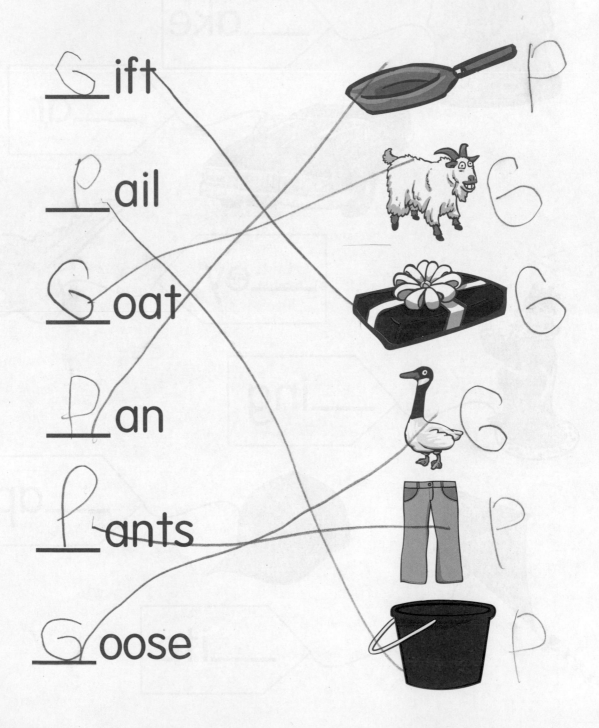

__G__ift

__P__ail

__G__oat

__P__an

__P__ants

__G__oose

Hooked on First Grade *Spelling Super Workbook*   © 2007 Educate Products, LLC

Mad Scramble

Unscramble the word that goes with each picture.
Write the word on the line.

neh

_____

ikd

_____

dahn

_____

tentik

_____

osueh

_____

ooragnak

_____

5

j or l?

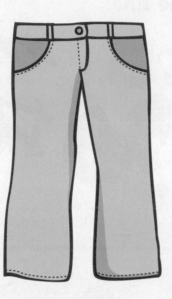

__eaf   __eans   __id

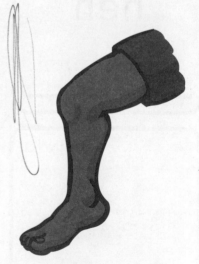

__am   __acket   __eg

What Is Missing?

I did it!

Write the word that completes each sentence.
Use the word box to help you.

| man | map | nap | net |

The _____ is in the cap.

The dog is taking a _____.

The nut is in the _____.

The _____ is standing.

7

qu or r?

Draw a line from each picture to the letter or letters that complete each word.

__Queen

__ring

__rabbit

qu   **r**

__Quarter

__rod

__Quilt

8

s or z?

Help Detective Dog get to the animal park.
Write an "s" or a "z" to complete each word.

__S__un

__Z__ebra

__S__eal

__Z__oo

9

Scavenger Hunt

This is a game for two or more players.

Look at the picture on the next page.

Take turns choosing a word from the box.

Spell the word out loud and find it in the picture.

Then see how many of the things you can find in your home.

Each time you find one, spell it.

bag	bed	box	cap	cat
cup	dot	duck	sock	sun

Where is that cup?

A Spelling Story

This is a game for two or more players.

Each player writes a story using five words from the list on the next page.

Make the story silly! Take turns reading the stories out loud.

Note to Parents

Children often have trouble learning to spell words whose first letter shares the same sound as another letter, such as "c" and "k." When learning to spell, children may also mix up letters that are next to each other in the alphabet, such as "m" and "n," or that look similar, such as "b" and "d." If your child has trouble spelling many of the words on the next page, try focusing on just a few words at a time.

Spell It!

This is a game for two players.

Copy each word from the list below onto an index card.

Mix the cards. Then pass them out so that each player has ten cards.

The first player reads the word on one of his cards out loud.

The other player guesses the spelling of the word.

If the player spells the word correctly, he gets to keep the card.

Keep taking turns until you have correctly spelled the words on all of the cards.

gift	sink
house	leg
box	queen
king	boy
map	nap
jeans	cake
girl	rabbit
drum	hand
zebra	pet
pan	car

Word Hunt

Look at each picture.

Say its name out loud.

Then circle the word in the puzzle.

Look across and down.

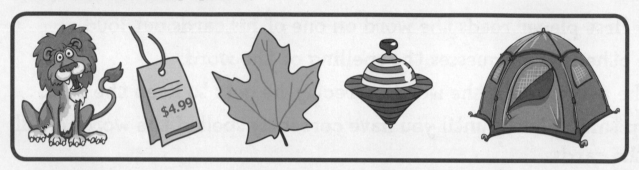

t   a   g   l

e   p   l   i

n   q   i   o

t   o   p   n

l   e   a   f

v or w?

Write a "v" or "w" to complete each word.
Then draw lines from each word to its matching picture.

__W__est

__W__ag

__V__iolin

__V__et

__W__eb

__W__ave

15

y or z?

Look at each picture. Write a "y" or "z" to complete each word.

__yarn__   __zebra__   __yellow__

__zipper__   __yo-yo__   __zoo__

What Is the Word?

Write the word that completes each sentence.
Use the word box to help you.

| bag | bat | pad | pan |

Cat holds a
__bat__.

Cat writes on a
__pad__ of
paper.

Cat has a
__bag__.

Cat looks for
a __pan__.

17

d or t?

Write a "d" or "t" to complete each word.
Draw lines to match each word to a picture.

_og	_esk	_ree
_ooth	_ire	_oll

Word Hunt

Circle each word you find in the puzzle.
Look across and down.

cab	coin	kick	kind	kitten
quack	queen	quick	quit	

q u i c k r

u b t o i p

a q u i t k

c a b n t i

k i n d e c

q u e e n k

19

Hooked on First Grade *Spelling Super Workbook*

Spelling Bingo

This is a game for three or more players.

You will need:

pencils

sheets of paper

one paper bag

game markers, such as pennies

How to play:

1. Make a bingo card for each player. Draw lines to divide a sheet of paper into 15 boxes. Draw an "X" in the center box.

2. Use the word list on the next page to fill the rest of the boxes. Each player writes the words in any order he chooses.

3. One player will act as the caller. The caller cuts his card apart, puts the words in the bag, and reads them out loud one at a time.

4. The other players use the game markers to cover the words on their cards.

The first player to cover a row across or down wins.

20

bag	net
cat	nut
dog	sink
doll	sock
fox	sun
map	van
mom	vest
nap	vet

Hooked on First Grade *Spelling Super Workbook*

Tongue Twisters

Say each tongue twister on the next page three times. See how fast you can say each one! Then write your own tongue twister on the lines. Choose some words from this list that begin with the same sound.

List:
big
bug
bit
bat
Mom
mopped
messy
milk

The dog ducked under the desk in the den.

The girl got a goose and a goat as a gift.

The seal saw the sea and the sun.

_____

_____

_____

_____

Note to Parents
Tongue twisters give your child practice with beginning sounds and letters. Together, think of tongue twisters you know. Help your child identify the beginning sound that is repeated and the letters that make that sound.

Hooked on First Grade *Spelling Super Workbook*

What an Ending!

Write "ad" or "ap" to complete each word.

n_____

s_____

m_____

c_____

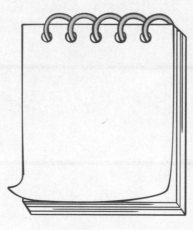
p_____

m_____

Hooked on First Grade *Spelling Super Workbook*

Make a Match

Write "an" or "at" to complete each word.
Then draw lines from each word to its matching picture.

h <u>at</u>

f <u>an</u>

v <u>an</u>

m <u>at</u>

c <u>at</u>

p <u>an</u>

25

Hooked on First Grade *Spelling Super Workbook*

What Is It?

Choose the word from the word box that best describes each picture. Then write the word on the line.

bag   cab   crab   flag
grab   rag   scab   tag

bag   cab   flag   scab

$4.99

tag   crab   rag   grab

Happy Endings

Draw a line from each picture to the letters that complete each word. Write the letters on the line.

p _an_   h _am_   f _an_

an   am

j _am_   r _am_   c _an_

Hooked on First Grade *Spelling Super Workbook*

What Is Missing?

Write the word that completes each sentence.
Use the word box to help you.

dip	kid	lid	sip

Take a __sip__.

Lift the __lid__.

Take a __dip__.

Hug a __kid__.

Nice Fin-ish!

Draw a line from each picture to the letters that complete the word.

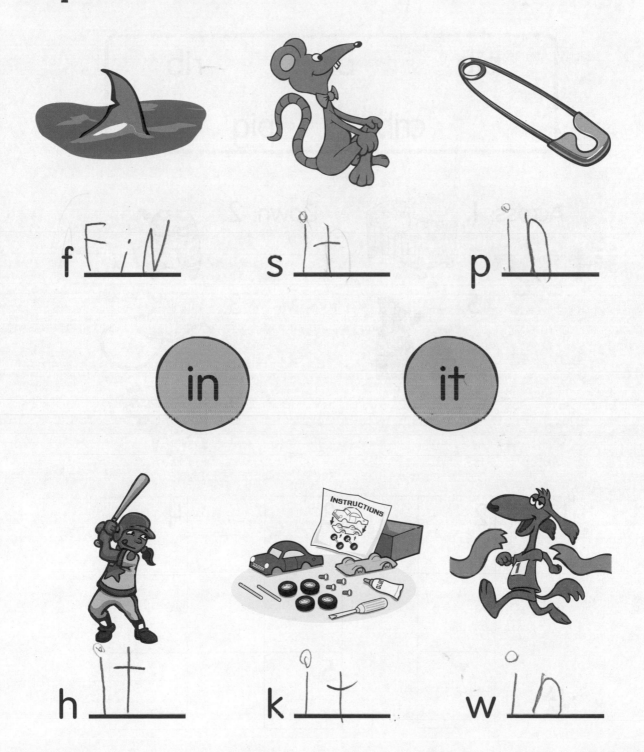

f __F i N__   s __i t__   p __i n__

in   **it**

h __i t__   k __i t__   w __i n__

29

Puzzle Time

Use the picture clues and the word box to fill in the puzzle.

bib	big	rib
crib		pig

Across: 1.    Down: 2.

5.    3.

4.

1	2		3		4
		5			

Rhyme Time

Color the word in each row that rhymes with the first word.

lid   lit   hid   sit

bit   lid   kid   sit

sit   kit   rid   lid

kid   lid   pit   sit

Hooked on First Grade *Spelling Super Workbook*

Picture This!

This is a game for two or more players.

You will need:
one coin
sheets of paper
pencils

How to play:

1. The first player flips the coin. If it lands on heads, draw a picture of a word from the Heads box on the next page. If it lands on tails, draw a picture of a word from the Tails box on the next page. The other players guess the word.

2. The next player flips the coin. He draws a picture of a different word from the Heads or the Tails box.

3. The players take turns until all of the words have been played.

32

Heads

van	hat	crab
lid	sit	fan

Tails

tag	lip	fin
pig	bib	kid

Sounds Like a Match

This is a game for two players.

You will need:

index cards

How to play:

1. Copy each word from column 1 on the next page onto its own index card. Then copy each word from column 2 onto its own card. Be careful to keep the column 1 and column 2 cards in separate piles.

2. Mix up the column 1 cards, and place them face down on a table in three rows of four cards each.

3. The first player turns over two cards. Do the words rhyme? If they do, they are a match! The player keeps the cards. If the words do not rhyme, the player turns both cards face down again. It is the next player's turn.

4. Keep taking turns until all of the matches have been made. Then play again with the pile of column 2 cards you did not use.

Note to Parents
Children love matching games, and this is a fun way to review several words with letter combinations that make the same sound. You and your child can brainstorm more words that have these phonograms to add new cards to your game. For an added challenge, brainstorm different phonograms.

Column 1	Column 2
glad	jam
sad	ham
gap	lip
lap	tip
can	bin
tan	fin
mat	dig
hat	big
bag	rib
tag	bib
cab	lid
jab	kid

Hooked on First Grade *Spelling Super Workbook*

Pick a Pot

Help Cat cook up some words.

Color the pot that completes each word.

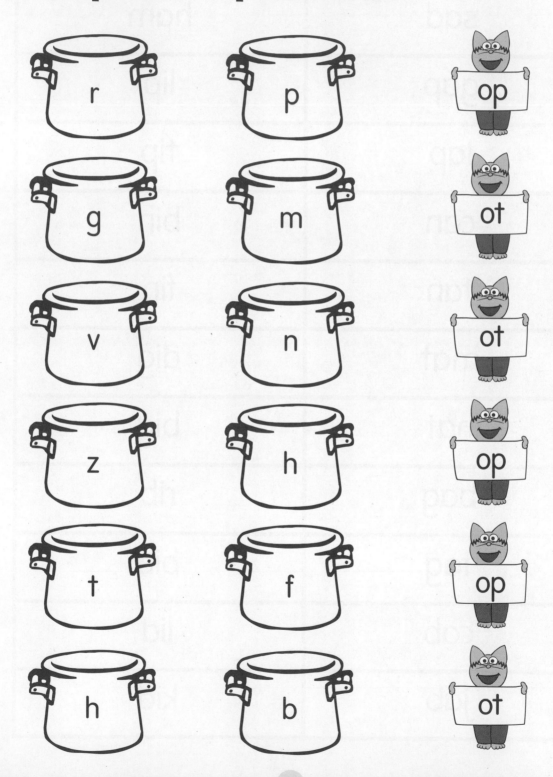

Hooked on First Grade *Spelling Super Workbook*

© 2007 Educate Products, LLC

What Is Missing?

Write the word that completes each sentence.
Use the word box to help you.

cob   job   pod   rod

Peas grow
in a __pod__ .

Being a vet
is his __job__ .

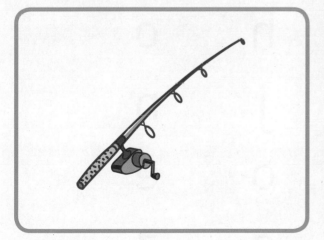

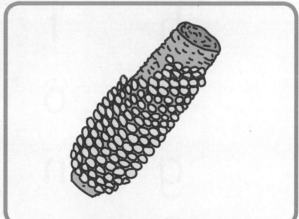

Fishermen
use a __rod__ .

Who ate the corn
on the __cob__ ?

37

Word Hunt

Circle each word you find in the puzzle.
Look across and down.

hog	fog	jog	son	ton	won

w	o	n	s
h	t	h	o
o	o	j	n
g	n	o	e
f	o	g	z

What an Ending!

Write "og" or "op" to complete each word.

d_OG_   st_OP_   t_OP_

m_OP_   l_OG_   fr_OG_

39

Story Time

Use the word box to help you complete each sentence in the story. Then read the story out loud.

mud   scrubs   suds   tub

Mad Dog rolls in the <u>mud</u>.

Next, Mad Dog gets in the <u>tub</u>.

Mad Dog <u>scrubs</u> with a lot of <u>suds</u>.

Now Mad Dog is clean again!

40

On the Farm

Spend time on the farm with Cat.

Color the hen that completes each word.

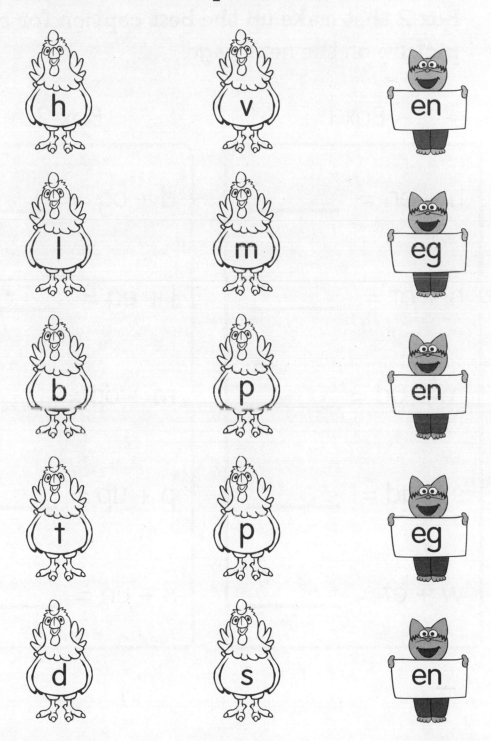

Hooked on First Grade *Spelling Super Workbook*

How Many Words?

1. Add the letters below to make words.

2. Choose the word from Box 1 and the word from Box 2 that make up the best caption for each picture on the next page.

Box 1   Box 2

h + en = _____   d + og = _____

h + ot = _____   l + eg = _____

m + ud = _____   m + op = _____

s + ad = _____   p + up = _____

w + et = _____   s + un = _____

1.

_____

2.

_____

3.

_____

4.

_____

5.

_____

Hooked on First Grade *Spelling Super Workbook*

What Is in a Word?

This is a game for two or more players.

How to play:

1. The first player calls out the sound made by one of the letter combinations on the next page.

2. The second player names something that ends with the same sound. The first player writes down the word on the chart on the next page.

3. Players take turns naming things that end with that sound, while the first player writes them down. When a player cannot think of anything else to name, another player calls out a new sound, and writes the things that are named on the chart.

Note to Parents
This game helps your child become familiar with different letter combinations that always make the same sound. Recognizing and pronouncing their sounds correctly is a large step forward in becoming a proficient writer and reader.

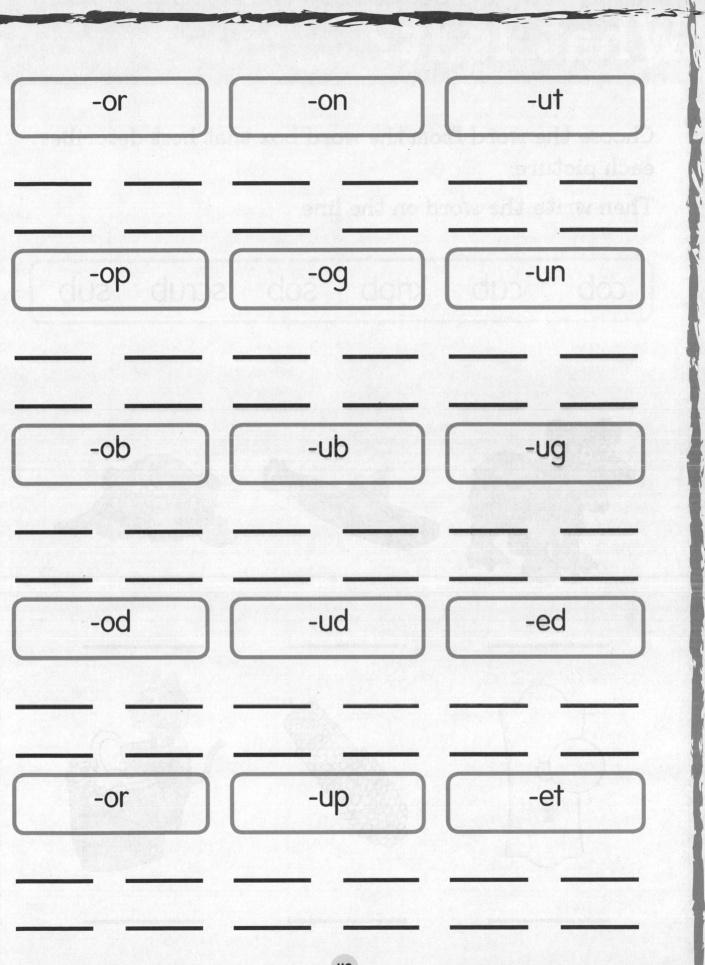

-or	-on	-ut

_____ _____ _____

_____ _____ _____

-op	-og	-un

_____ _____ _____

_____ _____ _____

-ob	-ub	-ug

_____ _____ _____

_____ _____ _____

-od	-ud	-ed

_____ _____ _____

_____ _____ _____

-or	-up	-et

_____ _____ _____

_____ _____ _____

What Is It?

Choose the word from the word box that best describes each picture.

Then write the word on the line.

| cob | cub | knob | sob | scrub | sub |

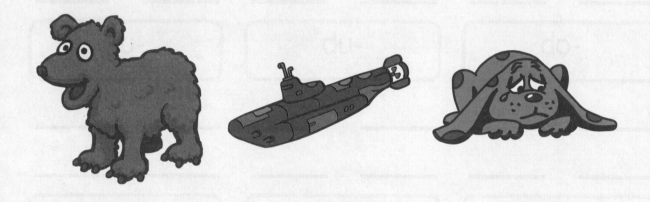

_____

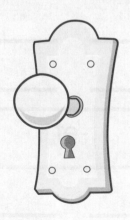  

_____

How Will It End?

Circle the ending that completes each word.

n	et	at
s	it	et
h	it	ut
p	at	ot
h	et	it
h	it	at

57

Say and Sort

This is a game for two players.

You will need:

twelve index cards

two paper bags

How to play:

1. Copy each word on the next page onto its own index card.

2. Put the cards with the words from the first column into one bag. Put the cards with the words from the second column into the other bag. Shake both bags to mix the cards.

3. The first player takes a card from each bag and says each word. If the words rhyme, take the cards out of the bags. If the words do not rhyme, place them face down in rows on a table. Players may then choose new cards from either the bags or the table.

4. Keep taking turns until all of the cards have been sorted into rhyming pairs.

pad	bad
can	ran
lip	dip
win	fin
fun	sun
hen	ten

Hooked on First Grade *Spelling Super Workbook*

A Book of Rhymes

Make your own book of rhymes.

Use the picture clues on the next page to write six pairs of rhyming words.

Write each of the rhymes on a sheet of paper.

Draw your own picture to go with each rhyme.

Staple your sheets together to make a book.

Note to Parents

This activity will give your child practice with spelling patterns, such as those found in *sun* and *run*, or *wet* and *pet*. Knowing these patterns will help your child read and spell many one-syllable words, along with longer words that contain these letter combinations. For extra practice, ask your child to think of and spell more words that rhyme with the words he is writing.

 in the

_____

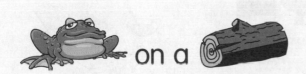 on a

 with a

_____

 in a

 in a

_____

Hooked on First Grade *Spelling Super Workbook*

Answer Key

PAGE 2

b̲ag d̲rum b̲at
b̲ee d̲ot d̲oor

PAGE 3
cake
car
key
king
cap
kite

PAGE 4

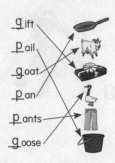

g̲ift
p̲ail
g̲oat
p̲an
p̲ants
g̲oose

PAGE 5
hen
kid
hand
kitten
house
kangaroo

PAGE 6
leaf
jeans
lid
jam
jacket
leg

PAGE 7
map
nap
net
man

PAGE 8

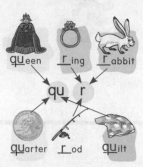

qu̲een r̲ing r̲abbit

qu r

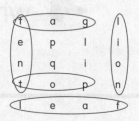

qu̲arter r̲od qu̲ilt

PAGE 9
sun
zebra
seal
zoo

PAGE 14

f	a	g		l
e	p	l		i
n	q	i		o
t	o	p		n
l	e	a	f	

PAGE 15

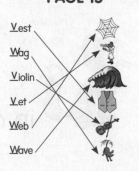

V̲est
W̲ag
V̲iolin
V̲et
W̲eb
W̲ave

PAGE 16
yarn
zebra
yellow
zipper
yo-yo
zoo

PAGE 17
bat
pad
bag
pan

PAGE 18

d̲og d̲esk t̲ree
t̲ooth t̲ire d̲oll

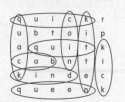

PAGE 19

q	u	i	c	k	r
u	b	t	o	i	p
a	q	u	i	t	k
c	a	b	n	t	i
k	i	n	d	i	c
q	u	e	e	n	k

PAGE 24
nap
sad
mad
cap
pad
map

PAGE 25

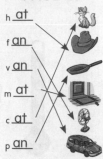

h̲ at
f̲ an
v̲ an
m̲ at
c̲ at
p̲ an

PAGE 26
bag
cab
flag
scab
tag
crab
rag
grab

PAGE 27

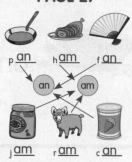

p̲ an h̲ am f̲ an
an am
j̲ am r̲ am c̲ an

PAGE 28
sip
lid
dip
kid

PAGE 29

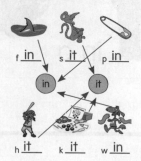

f̲ in s̲ it p̲ in
in it
h̲ it k̲ it w̲ in

62

PAGE 30

Across:

1. crib

5. big

Down:

2. rib

3. bib

4. pig

PAGE 31

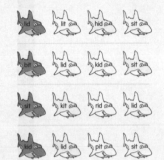
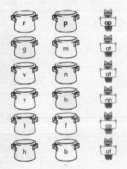

PAGE 36

PAGE 37

pod

job

rod

cob

PAGE 38

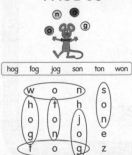

hog fog jog son ton won

PAGE 39

dog

stop

top

mop

log

frog

PAGE 40

mud

tub

scrubs

suds

PAGE 41

c up   n ut

up   ut

p up   c ut

PAGE 42

mug

rug

run

fun

PAGE 43

Across:

2. cut

3. rut

4. tub

Down:

1. hut

2. cub

3. rub

PAGE 44

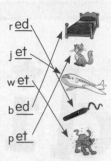
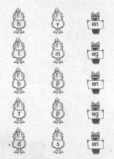

r ed

j et

w et

b ed

p et

PAGE 45

h   v   en

l   m   eg

b   p   en

t   p   eg

d   s   en

PAGE 46-47

1. hot sun

2. sad pup

3. mud dog

4. hen leg

5. wet mop

PAGE 50

cub

sub

sob

knob

cob

scrub

PAGE 51

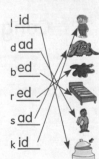

l id

d ad

b ed

r ed

s ad

k id

PAGE 52

bag; wig;
dig; pig;
dog; rag;
log; tag

PAGE 53

hug

fed

tug

led or lug

shed

PAGE 54

f a n v b
i q p a n
n u i n c
c a n o d
g r i n x

PAGE 55

bun; men; Ben;
hen; ten; fun;
run

PAGE 56

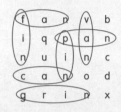

dip nap mop pit cap
pup lap sip top

w r p m o p
x p f s l k
d i p c a p
z t o p p n
v m n u r a
s i p p r l

PAGE 57

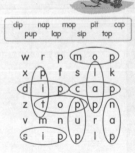

n   et   at

s   it   et

h   it   ut

p   at   ot

h   et   it

h   it   at

63

Hooked on First Grade *Spelling Super Workbook*

I did it!

Congratulations!

_____

- - - - - - - - - - - - - - - - - - - -

_____

has successfully completed this chapter.

Ist Grade
Hooked on Phonics®
Spelling

Chapter 2

b or d?

Write a "b" or "d" to complete each word.

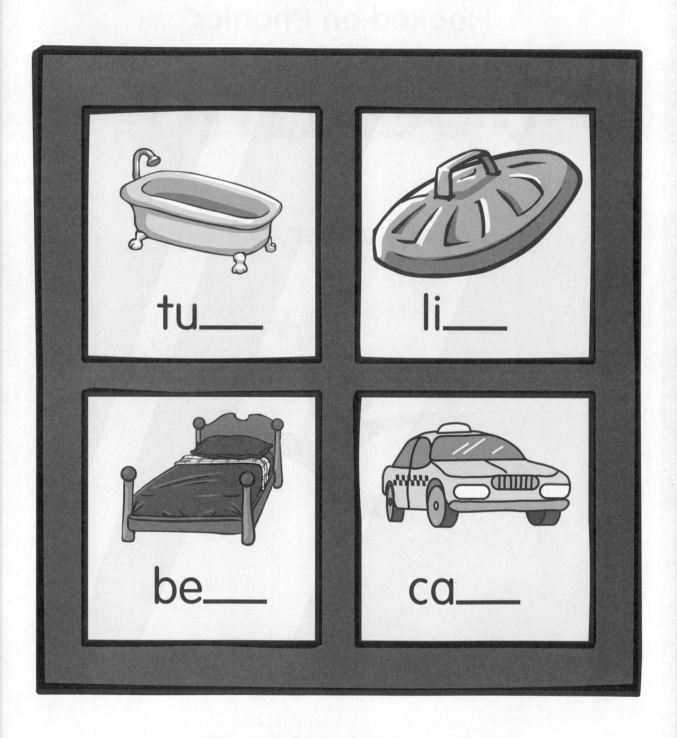

tu___

li___

be___

ca___

Player 1

jet	top	hum
cat	pup	bed

Player 2

ed	fit	tip
but	not	jet

Fix It

Help the Ratini Brothers sort letters.

Write "x" or "ck" to complete each word.

Color the "x" mailboxes red.

Color the "ck" mailboxes blue.

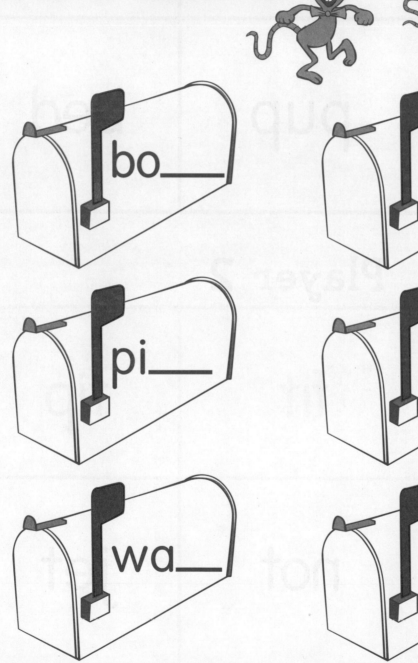

bo____

fi____

pi____

sa____

wa____

lu____

Hooked on First Grade *Spelling Super Workbook*

A Bag of Rhymes

This is a game for two or more players.

How to play:

1. Copy each word on the list onto an index card. Put the cards in a paper bag.

2. The first player picks a card from the bag and says the word out loud.

3. The player thinks of a rhyming word. If he makes the rhyme, he keeps the card.

4. Now the next player gets a turn. Keep taking turns until all of the cards are out of the bag. The player with the most cards wins.

class	miss	guess
loss	sniff	huff
cluck	ax	mix
kick	rack	dock

Note to Parents

If your child has trouble thinking of a rhyme—and thinking of rhymes for some of these words can be challenging—play a variation of the game giving three word choices. For example, if your child draws the card with the word "sniff," you could say, What rhymes with sniff: cliff, hiss, or six?

tap

hiss

skip

hum

buzz

hop

Hooked on First Grade *Spelling Super Workbook*

Hot or Cold?

Go on a family treasure hunt. Point to a letter on this page.

Think of things in your home that have short vowel sounds, such as cap, pen, pin, sock, and rug.

Write the words on the lines on the next page.

a

i

o

e

u

Collect the objects that you and your child wrote down.

Hide those objects!

Can other family members find each object on the list?

Say "hot" if the person is heading in the right direction.

Say it louder the closer he gets.

Say "cold" if the person goes in the wrong direction.

Have your child make a check next to each word as it is found.

_____   _____

_____   _____

_____   _____

_____   _____

Note to Parents
This activity will help your child learn to read words that contain short vowel sounds. As you write down each word, encourage your child to sound it out. Invite your child to write down each of the words on index cards. Afterward, have him draw a picture of each object on the other side of the card.

Hooked on First Grade *Spelling Super Workbook*

The Hat Fits!

Find and say words with an "a" in them.
Color those parts of the hat red.
Find and say words with an "i" in them.
Color those parts of the hat green.

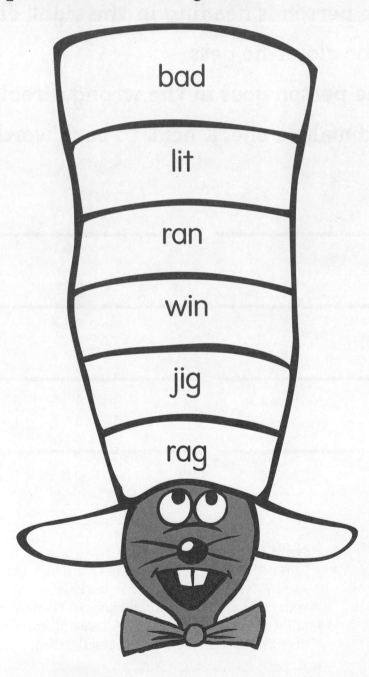

bad

lit

ran

win

jig

rag

Mixed up Balloons

Write a "u" or an "e" to complete each word.
Is the word the same as the word on the balloon?
Follow the strings to see if you are right.

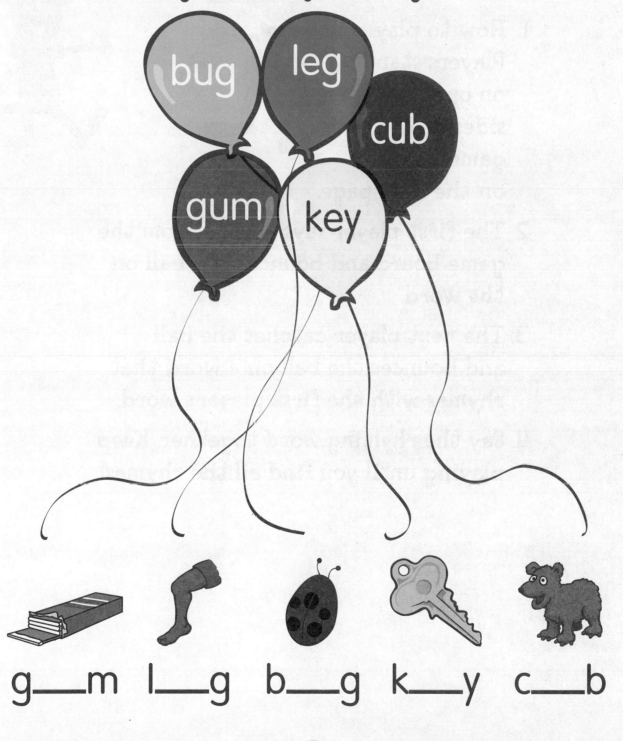

g__m   l__g   b__g   k__y   c__b

109

Word Bounce

This is a game for two or more players.

You will need:
a small ball

1. How to play: Players stand on opposite sides of the game board on the next page.

2. The first player says a word from the game board and bounces the ball on the word.

3. The next player catches the ball and bounces the ball on a word that rhymes with the first player's word.

4. Say the rhyming word together. Keep playing until you find all the rhymes!

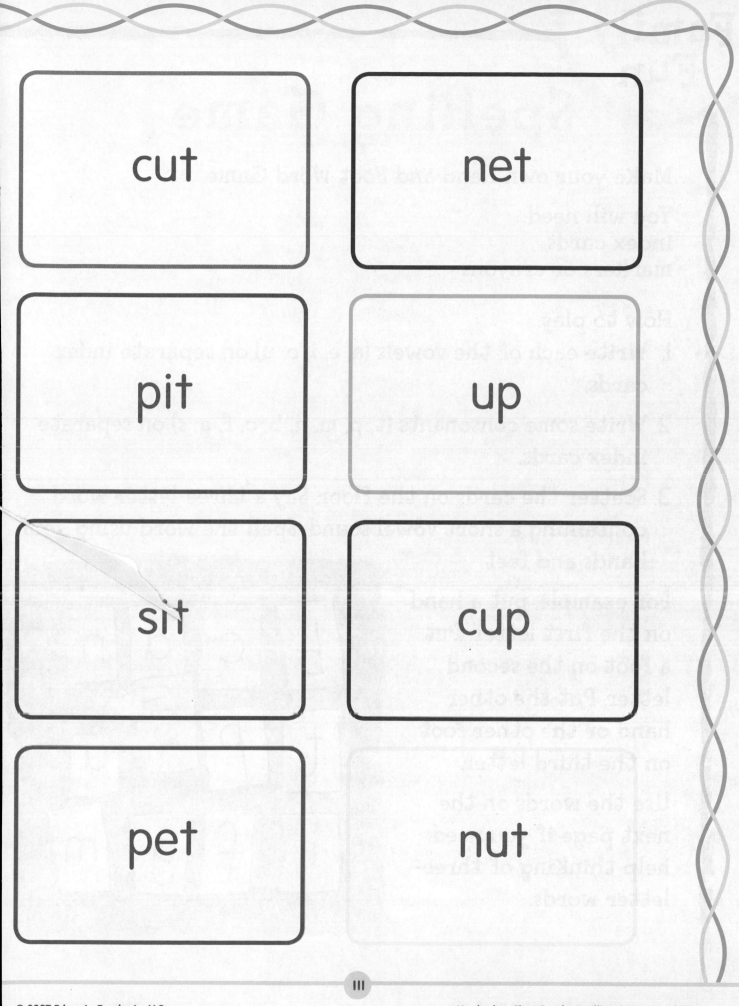

cut

net

pit

up

sit

cup

pet

nut

Spelling Game

Make your own Hand and Foot Word Game.

You will need:
index cards
markers or crayons

How to play:

1. Write each of the vowels (a, e, i, o, u) on separate index cards.

2. Write some consonants (t, p, m, n, b, c, f, g, s) on separate index cards.

3. Scatter the cards on the floor. Say a three-letter word containing a short vowel sound. Spell the word using your hands and feet.

For example, put a hand on the first letter. Put a foot on the second letter. Put the other hand or the other foot on the third letter.

Use the words on the next page if you need help thinking of three-letter words.

Ten Bub__es

Say each word.

Find four words that ____ __e with "hen."

Color those bubbles re____

Find six words that rhy__ __e with "fan."

Color those bubbles blue___

ten

__un

tan

van

pen

den

man

can

pan

men

115

Cloud Colors

Say the word on the first cloud in each row.
Find the word in the same row that rhymes.
Color those clouds the same color.

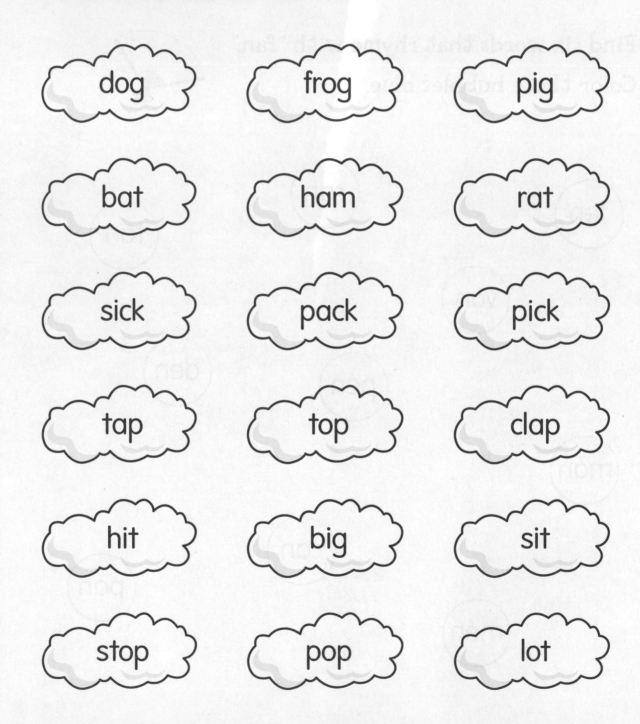

dog   frog   pig

bat   ham   rat

sick   pack   pick

tap   top   clap

hit   big   sit

stop   pop   lot

Middle Rhymes

Help the Ratini Brother pull things out of his hat.

Write a letter to complete each word.

Use the letter box to help you.

Say each word out loud.

Draw lines between the words that rhyme.

a e i

ch ____ ss

k ____ ss

gl ____ ss

dr ____ ss

h ____ ss

gr ____ ss

121

Rhyme It!

This is a game for two or more players.

How to play:

1. Drop a coin on the board on the next page.

2. Say the word the coin landed on.

3. Take turns saying a word that rhymes.

How many rhyming words can you think of?

Hooked on First Grade *Spelling Super Workbook*

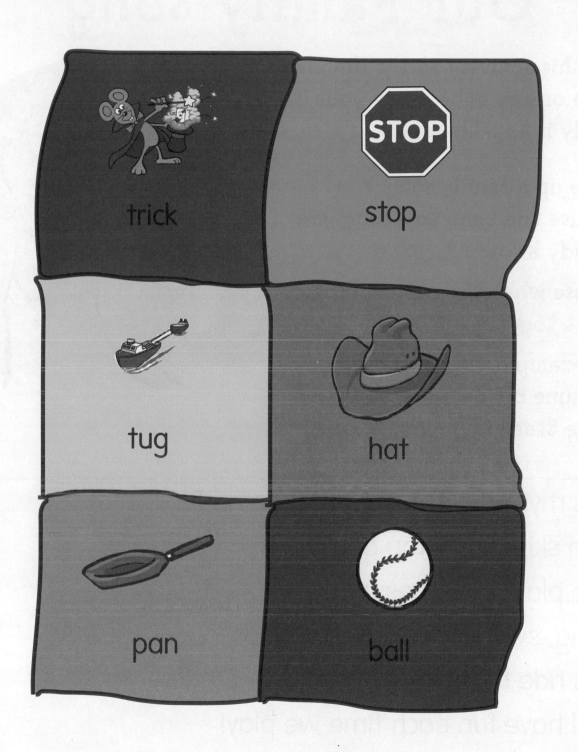

trick

stop

tug

hat

pan

ball

123

Our Family Song

Try this activity at the dinner table or any other time your family is together.

Make up a family song. You can use the tune to a song you already know.

Choose what the song will be about together.

For example, sing this song to the tune of "Twinkle, Twinkle, Little Star."

Let's rhyme words and have some fun.

I can skip and jump and run!

I like playing games with you—

hiking, swimming, baseball, too.

Let's ride bikes on Saturday.

We'll have fun each time we play!

See how many songs your family can make up!

Write your song here.

Use another piece of paper if you need more room.

_____

_____

_____

_____

_____

_____

_____

Note to Parents

Your song can be silly, sweet, or rock 'n' roll. Use a tape recorder to record your song. Sing the first line. Help your child sing the next line, ending with a rhyming word. Ask your child to think of other rhyming lyrics. Sing the third line and help your child sing the fourth line, again ending with a word that rhymes. Sing alternating lines until you reach the end of the song.

Answer Key

PAGE 66
tub; lid; bed; cab

PAGE 67
bug; cub; bib; flag

PAGE 68
log; hid; pig; tug; pad; mad

PAGE 69

PAGE 70
Across
2. man
3. ham
4. ten
Down
1. jam
2. man
3. hen

PAGE 71
ten; jam; tin; ham; him; fan

PAGE 72
bat; cap; mop; pup; nut

PAGE 73
ma___ p t
pi___ p t
nu___ p t
ne___ p t
li___ p t
cu___ p t

PAGE 74

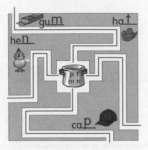
gu**m**   ha**t**
he**n**
p
m n
ca**p**

PAGE 75
Across
2. men
3. hot
4. rip
Down
1. net
2. mop
3. hit

PAGE 78
bo**x**   fi**x**
pi**ck**   sa**ck**
wa**x**   lu**ck**

PAGE 79

 fo   ck   x
 du   **ck**   x
 pi   **ck**   x
 bo   ck   **x**
 sti   **ck**   x

PAGE 80

bu**zz**   o**ff**
hu**ff**   fi**zz**

PAGE 81
hiss; pass; puff; off

PAGE 82

buzz   dress   glass   jazz

Bees can do it. It rhymes with "fuzz." They fly around and sound like __buzz__.	A girl wears one. It rhymes with "mess." It's not a skirt. It's a __dress__.
These brothers play it. It rhymes with "razz." It is sound that we call __jazz__.	You drink from it. It rhymes with "pass." You can see through it. It is a __glass__.

PAGE 83

fo__x__
so__ck__
dre__ss__
clo__ck__
bo__x__
ki__ss__

PAGE 88

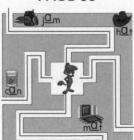
j**a**m   h**a**t
c**a**n
m**a**t

PAGE 89

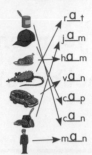
r**a**t
j**a**m
h**a**m
v**a**n
c**a**p
c**a**n
m**a**n

PAGE 90
bib; big; pit; wig; kit

PAGE 91
him; sit; pin; lip; dip; fit

PAGE 92
top; doll; dot; pot; cob; frog

PAGE 93
hot; top; pop; cob; nod

PAGE 94
Across
2. bug
3. hut
4. mud
Down
1. nut
2. bud
3. hug

PAGE 95
tub; bun; bus; pup; rug

126

PAGE 96

(pet)

jet

pen

(vet)

hen

net

PAGE 97

Answers will vary: Possible answers include set, pen, ten, net, get, pet.

PAGE 102

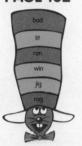

bad
lit
ran
win
jig
rag

PAGE 103

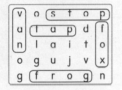

PAGE 104

PAGE 105

pup; bug; big; nut; pig

PAGE 106

Answers will vary. Possible answers include ten, pen, bed, led, sit, pit, bit, dip, tip, sip, lip.

PAGE 107

cup-pup; sun-fun; rug-hug; box-fox; log-fog; pot-hot

PAGE 108

Across:

2. pen

3. cot

4. mop

Down:

1. jet

2. dad

3. cow

PAGE 109

gum; leg; bug; key; cub

PAGE 114

PAGE 115

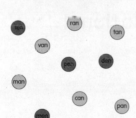

PAGE 116

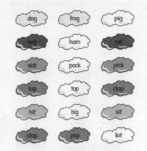

PAGE 117

rug; box; mat; net; wig

PAGE 118

PAGE 119

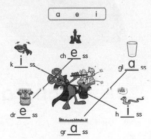

PAGE 120

truck; clock; brick; pack

PAGE 121

Hooked on First Grade *Spelling Super Workbook*

I did it!

Congratulations!

_____

- - - - - - - - - - - - - - - - - -

_____

has successfully completed this chapter.

Ist Grade

Hooked on Phonics®

Spelling

Chapter 3

Sound It Out!

Look at each picture.

Write "sc," "sk," or "st" to complete each word.

___ ___ull ___ ___ar ___ ___arf

___ ___amp ___ ___ale ___ ___unk

Color the Cheese!

I did it!

Help the Ratini make some words.

Color the cheese that completes each word.

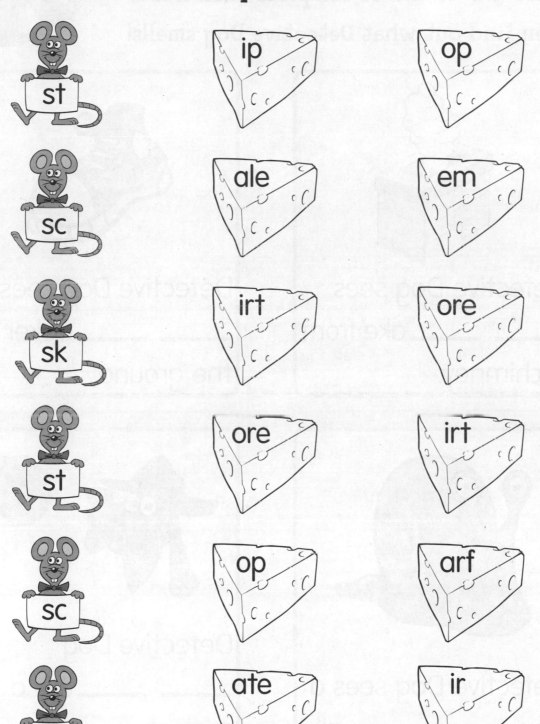

st   ip   op

sc   ale   em

sk   irt   ore

st   ore   irt

sc   op   arf

sk   ate   ir

Hooked on First Grade *Spelling Super Workbook*

Follow the Trail!

Follow Detective Dog's trail.

Write "sm" or "sn" to complete each word.

Then find out what Detective Dog smells!

Detective Dog sees _____ _____oke from a chimney.

Detective Dog sees a _____ _____eaker on the ground.

Detective Dog sees a slow _____ _____ail.

Detective Dog _____ _____ells a cookie!

Search for Words!

Detective Dog is searching for words that start with "sm" or "sn."

Circle each word you find in the puzzle. Look across and down.

small	smell	smoke
snap	sneak	snow

s	m	a	l	l	r	s
n	d	s	n	a	p	m
e	o	n	u	h	w	o
a	q	o	a	s	g	k
k	z	w	p	c	y	e
x	f	s	m	e	l	l

Hooked on First Grade *Spelling Super Workbook*

Swish Goes the Brush!

The Ratini Brothers painted pictures.

Look at each picture.

Write "sl," "sp," or "sw" to complete each word.

___ ___ed   ___ ___oon   ___ ___an

___ ___ider   ___ ___ing   ___ ___ide

134

New Caps for Cat

Cat lost his cap.

Color the cap that completes each word.

    ip

    ace

    eeve

    in

    amp

    ug

135

Spin, Skip, or Snore!

This is a game for two or more players.

You will need:

one coin

How to play:

1. The first player flips the coin.

2. He acts out a word in the Heads box on the next page if the coin lands on heads. He acts out a word in the Tails box if it lands on tails. The other players guess the word and spell it.

3. The second player flips the coin. He acts out a different word from the Heads or Tails box.

4. The players take turns until all of the words have been acted out.

136

Heads

skip	snore	smell
spin	sweep	skate

Tails

scare	slide	stack
sweat	spy	sneak

Hooked on First Grade *Spelling Super Workbook*

Tell Me a Story

This is a game for two or more players.

Use words from the list on the next page to write a story together.

Each player chooses five words from the list.

The first player writes a sentence using one of his five words. The next player adds another sentence using one of his five words. Keep taking turns and adding sentences until all the words have been used. Try to make the sentences flow together as a story.

Take turns reading your story out loud.

Note to Parents
This activity gives your child an opportunity not only to practice the spelling words in the book, but also to be imaginative and think creatively. If your child knows other words that begin with these consonant blends, encourage him to use these words in the story as well.

138

scare	slip	spin
scoop	small	spy
score	smart	stage
scout	smell	star
skate	smile	start
ski	snake	stop
skirt	sneak	store
skunk	sneeze	swallow
sky	snow	swim
sled	snuggle	swing

bl, pl, or gl?

Write "bl," "pl," or "gl" to complete each word.

___ ___ane   ___ ___ocks   ___ ___obe

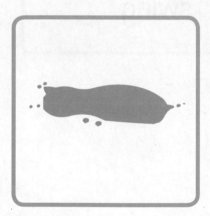

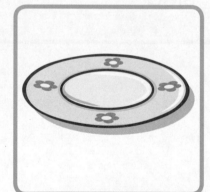

___ ___ue   ___ ___ove   ___ ___ate

Don't Blink!

The Ratini is doing magic.

Write the word that completes each sentence. Use the word box to help you. Find out what the Ratini pulled from his magic hat.

| blanket | glass | plant | plug |

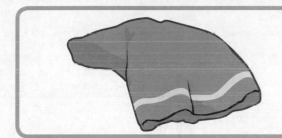

The Ratini pulled a _____ out of his hat.

Then the Ratini pulled a _____ out of his hat.

There was a _____ in his hat too.

The last thing he pulled out was a _____.

141

Clap for a Match!

Write "fl," "cl," or "sl" to complete each word.
Draw lines to match each word to a picture.

___ ___ower

___ ___ock

___ ___ippers

___ ___oud

___ ___ag

___ ___ide

Hooked on First Grade *Spelling Super Workbook*

Make Some Words!

This is a game for two players.

You will need:

index cards

a pencil

a piece of paper

f-l-y spells fly

How to play:

1. Copy pairs of letters from the box below onto separate index cards. Place them in a pile face down.

bl	br	cl	cr	dr
fl	fr	pl	tr	

2. Write the word endings from the next page onto separate index cards. Place the cards face up on a table.

3. Flip over a card with beginning letters. Make a word using this card and one of the word ending cards. Write your word down on a piece of paper.

4. Place the beginning letters card at the bottom of the pile. Take turns making words and adding them to your list.

156

ock	y
ain	ip
ade	ap
ug	ag
ib	ane
ap	og
ush	ess
ack	um

Note to Parents

This activity is a good way for your child to learn how to sound out, read, and spell words with beginning consonant blends. Once your child has written several words on the sheet of paper, have him choose five words from the list. Together, write a story using these words. Afterward, encourage your child to read the story out loud.

mp or nd?

Write "mp" or "nd" to complete each word.

ha____

la____

ba____

ju____

wa____

hu____

nt, ft, lt, and st

I did it!

Complete the words. Draw lines to match the beginning letters on the apples to the ending letters on the bags.

se

so

sa

nt

ft

lt

st

fa

gi

la

Hooked on First Grade *Spelling Super Workbook*

Rhyme Time!

This is a game for two players.

You will need:

one coin

How to play:

1. The first player flips the coin. If it lands on heads, read a word in the Heads box on the next page. If it lands on tails, read a word in the Tails box on the next page. The other player says a word that rhymes. Look in the Rhyme Bank for help.

2. The second player flips the coin. He reads a different word from the Heads or Tails box.

3. The players take turns until they have said a rhyme for each word.

Rhyme Bank

sent	lift	draft	mint
pest	last	twist	hand
find	send	stamp	lump

Heads

tent	gift	raft
hint	best	fast

Tails

list	stand	mind
bend	lamp	bump

Write a Rhyme

This is a game for two or more players.

Each player chooses three pairs of rhyming words from the list on the next page.

Write a silly sentence with each pair of words.

Then take turns reading the sentences aloud.

Note to Parents
Learning common word endings helps build children's reading vocabulary. Once your child knows the word *best,* he can more easily recognize *vest, zest, rest, nest,* and so on. Read each pair of words aloud, and help your child point to the letters that match.

Play a Card Game

This is a game for two players.

Copy each word from the word box onto its own index card.

Place the cards face down in rows on a table.

The first player turns over two cards. If they rhyme, he keeps the pair. If not, he turns the cards over again. Keep taking turns until each card has been matched.

best	vest
fast	last
twist	list
band	hand
kind	find
bend	send
lamp	stamp
bump	lump
draft	raft
gift	lift
bent	dent
hint	mint

Add an s

Write an "s" at the end of each word to show that there is more than one.

bear___   gift___

bat___   crab___

coat___   net___

174

How Does It End?

Help Mad Dog find the right ending.

Circle the book that completes each word.

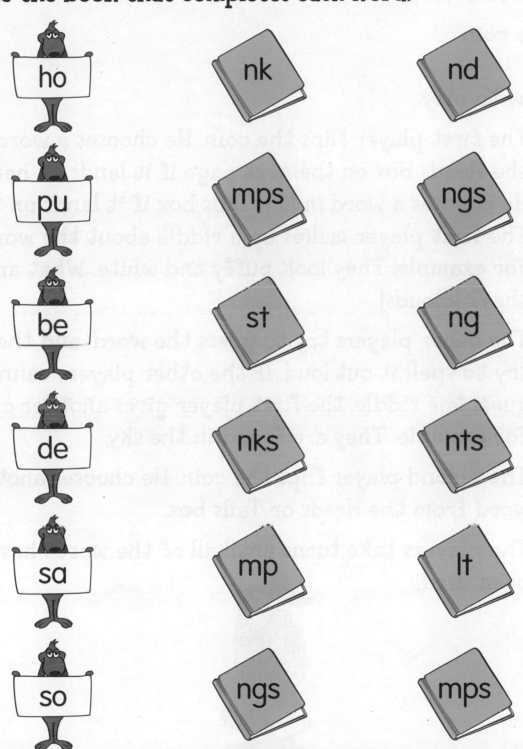

ho   nk   nd

pu   mps   ngs

be   st   ng

de   nks   nts

sa   mp   lt

so   ngs   mps

185

Read It and Guess It

This is a game for two or more players.

You will need:

one coin

How to play:

1. The first player flips the coin. He chooses a word in the Heads box on the next page if it lands on heads. He chooses a word in the Tails box if it lands on tails. The first player makes up a riddle about the word. For example: They look puffy and white. What are they? [clouds]

2. The other players try to guess the word, and then try to spell it out loud. If the other players cannot guess the riddle, the first player gives another clue. For example: They are found in the sky.

3. The second player flips the coin. He chooses another word from the Heads or Tails box.

4. The players take turns until all of the words have been used.

186

Heads

gloves	drums	clouds
planes	blocks	prizes

Tails

clowns	trucks	trains
stairs	swings	stars

Hooked on First Grade *Spelling Super Workbook*

Hunt for Words

Look inside your home or out in your yard for words that begin with consonant blends, such as "fl," "st," "cl," "br," "pl," and "gr." When you find something that begins with one of the blends, write the word on the lines on the next page. Keep searching until you have marked all of the boxes. If you have trouble finding things, ask a family member for help.

fl

_____

_____

_____

cl

_____

_____

_____

pl

_____

_____

_____

st

_____

_____

_____

br

_____

_____

_____

gr

_____

_____

_____

189

Answer Key

PAGE 130
skull
star
scarf
stamp
scale
skunk

PAGE 131
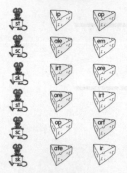
st | ip | op
sc | ale | em
sk | irt | ore
st | ore | irt
sc | op | arf
sk | ate | ir

PAGE 132
smoke
sneaker
snail
smells

PAGE 133
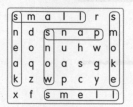

s	m	a	l	l	r	s
n	d	s	n	a	p	m
e	o	n	u	h	w	o
a	q	o	a	s	g	k
k	z	w	p	c	y	e
x	f	s	m	e	l	l

PAGE 134
sled
spoon
swan
spider
swing
slide

PAGE 135

sl | sp | sw | ip
sl | sp | sw | ace
sl | sp | sw | eeve
sl | sp | sw | in
sl | sp | sw | amp
sl | sp | sw | ug

PAGE 140

p l ___ ane
b l ___ ocks
g l ___ obe

b l ___ ue
g l ___ ove
p l ___ ate

PAGE 141
blanket
glass
plug
plant

PAGE 142
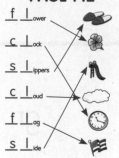
f l ___ ower
c l ___ ock
s l ___ ippers
c l ___ oud
f l ___ ag
s l ___ ide

PAGE 143
slide
floor
clown
flat
cloud
slice
clam

PAGE 144
dress
bricks
present
bread
drum
princess

PAGE 145
br
broom
brown
pr
press
price
dr
drip
draw

PAGE 146
grasshopper
crayon
grapes
crab

PAGE 147
crib
grass
cry
grin

PAGE 148

fr | tr | own
fr | tr | ack
fr | tr | unk
fr | tr | eeze
fr | tr | ash
fr | tr | ade
fr | tr | ame

PAGE 149
train
frame
tree
frown
trumpet

PAGE 150
bread
blanket
bricks
blocks
broom
blue

PAGE 151
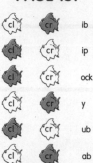
cl | cr | ib
cl | cr | ip
cl | cr | ock
cl | cr | y
cl | cr | ub
cl | cr | ab

PAGE 152
fruit
flag
frog
fly

PAGE 153
grapes
present
glove
plate
unscrambled word:
plum

PAGES 156–157
Answers will vary.
Possible words
include block, brush,
clap, crush, dress,
flap, fry, plain, and
train.

PAGE 158
hand
lamp
band
jump
wand
hump

190

PAGE 159

bu	mp	ft
ki	ft	nd
so	nd	ft
sa	nd	mp
ca	ft	mp
fi	nd	ft

PAGE 160

cast
nest
melt
ghost
belt

PAGE 161

l	a	s	t	r
g	q	s	e	h
i	f	a	s	t
f	e	l	t	r
t	m	t	o	p

PAGE 162

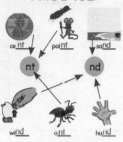

ce nt   pai nt   sa nd

nt   nd

wi nd   a nt   ha nd

PAGE 163

plant-ant
band-land
tent-went
pond-blond

PAGE 164

ring
king
bank
ink
link
swing

PAGE 165

sing
sink
trunk
king

PAGE 166

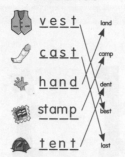

u e s t
c a s t
h a n d
s t a m p
t e n t

land
camp
dent
best
last

PAGE 167

list	twist	last
kind	send	find
bump	lamp	lump
hint	hand	mint
draft	raft	gift
sent	ramp	dent
land	hand	lost

PAGE 168

ce	nd	ng	nk	nt
ha	nd	ng	nk	nt
sku	nd	ng	nk	nt
swi	nd	ng	nk	nt
a	nd	ng	nk	nt
tru	nd	ng	nk	nt

PAGE 169

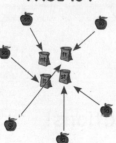

PAGE 174

bears
gifts
bats
crabs
coats
nets

PAGE 175

bugs
bags
houses
cones
pins
rugs

PAGE 176

boxes
foxes
dishes
brushes
watches
lunches

PAGE 177

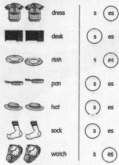

b	u	s	h	e	s	
b	o	x	e	s		f
m	a	p	s	e		o
p	i	g	r	a		x
b	u	s	e	s		e
d	i	s	h	e	s	s

PAGE 178

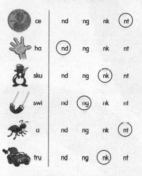

dress	s	es
desk	s	es
dish	s	es
pan	s	es
hat	s	es
sock	s	es
watch	s	es

PAGE 179

buses
bushes
chairs
dogs
dresses
pins
glasses
shops

PAGE 180

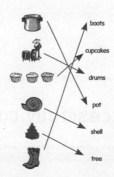

boots
cupcakes
drums
pot
shell
tree

PAGE 181

| lampS | handS | beltS |
| plantS | tankS | ghostS |

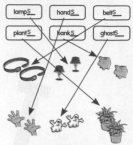

PAGE 182

steps
stars
slides
sleds
snakes
stamps

PAGE 183

trees
flags
cribs
flowers
presents
frogs

PAGE 184

ring
wings
ants
tent
plant
kings

PAGE 185

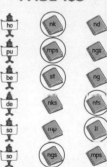

ho	nk	nd
pu	mps	ngs
be	st	ng
de	nks	nts
sa	mp	ll
so	ngs	mps

191

I did it!

Congratulations!

_____

- - - - - - - - - - - - - - - - - - - -

_____

has successfully completed this chapter.

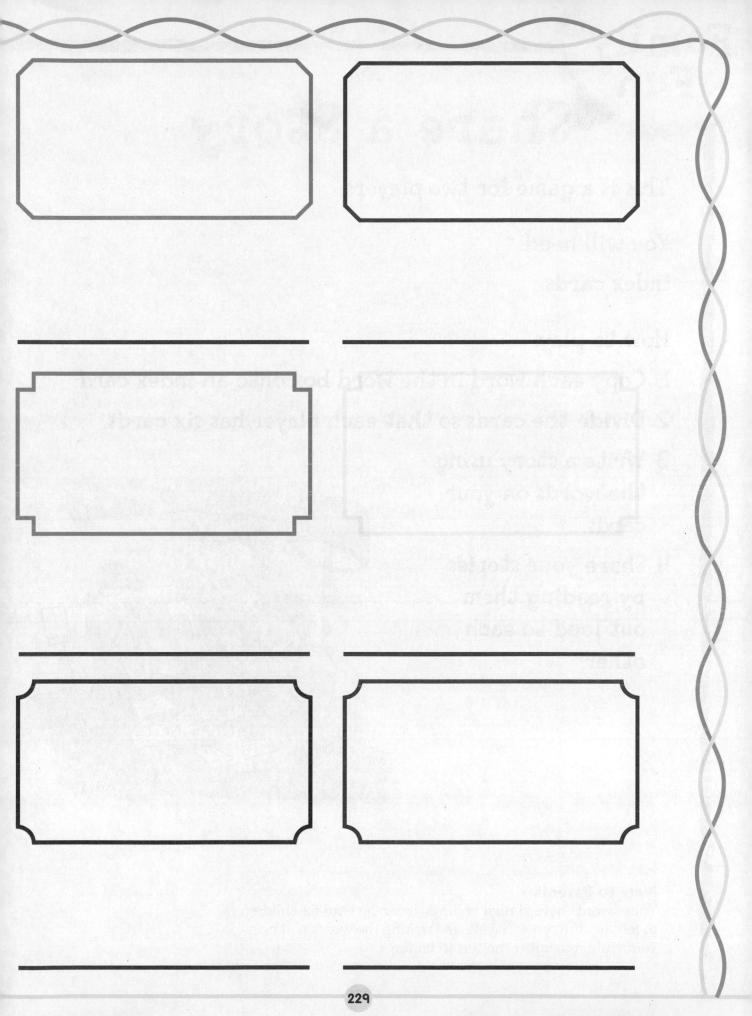

_____

_____

_____

_____

_____

_____

Hooked on First Grade *Spelling Super Workbook*

Share a Story

This is a game for two players.

You will need:

index cards

How to play:

1. Copy each word in the word box onto an index card.

2. Divide the cards so that each player has six cards.

3. Write a story using the words on your cards.

4. Share your stories by reading them out loud to each other.

Note to Parents
These words have similar endings. It can be hard for children to tell the difference. Saying and writing the words will help your child remember the correct endings.

beach   both   brush   catch   dish   itch

much   path   wash   watch   which   with

Hooked on First Grade *Spelling Super Workbook*

Just the Right Person!

Adding "er" to these "action" words turns them into "people" words. Each new word changes what Mad Dog and Cat are doing into who they are.

Write "er" on the lines to change each word.

box __ __

pitch __ __

camp __ __

catch __ __

paint __ __

wash __ __

Hooked on First Grade *Spelling Super Workbook*

Who Is It?

Write the word that describes each picture.

Use the word box to help you.

camper   painter   player   singer

_____

_____

GO CAT!

_____

_____

233

Match It

Write "er" on the lines to form a new word.

Draw a line from each word to its matching picture.

climb__ __

bath__ __

work__ __

box__ __

catch__ __

farm__ __

Gift Giver

Help Cat label the presents.

Look at the picture on each tag. Then write the word that matches. Use the word box to help you.

mother   father   brother   sister

_____

_____

_____

_____

235

© 2007 Educate Products, LLC

Hooked on First Grade *Spelling Super Workbook*

Finished at Last

These words need the letters "ed" to show that they happened already.

Write "ed" at the end of each word.

sail____

fish____

cook____

spill____

walk____

paint____

wash____

finish____

Missed Words

Write the word that completes each sentence.
Use the word box to help you.

> licked   packed
>
> looked   played

Detective Dog _____ at the letters.

Detective Dog _____ his bag.

Detective Dog _____ his lips.

Detective Dog _____ some music.

Mad Dog's Day

Mad Dog had a busy day! Draw a line from each word to the picture that shows what Mad Dog did.

painted

fished

camped

rested

walked

washed

238

Prepared for a Picnic

Help Mad Dog get to the picnic. Draw a path through the words that end in "ed."

end · sing · ring

pitch · talked · buzz

wait · played · washed

wish · START · fished · itched

pill · brush · cooked · painted

float · reach · finished

239

Thinking about ing

Write "ing" on each line to describe what Detective Dog is doing in each picture. Then write a sentence using one of the "ing" words.

sleep_____

read_____

yawn _____

pack_____

look_____

think_____

_____

_____.

What's Missing?

Write the word that completes each sentence.
Use the word box to help you.

| drinking | flying | holding | standing |

Cat and Mad Dog
are _____
the plane.

This rat is
_____
on the mat.

Cat is
_____
the bag.

Mad Dog is
_____
some milk.

241

Keeping Busy

Look at each picture. Write an "ing" word that describes what Mad Dog is doing.

Use the word box to help you.

| boxing | catching | painting |
| resting | sailing | splashing |

_____   _____   _____

_____   _____   _____

Hunting for Words

Circle each word you find in the puzzle.

Look across and down.

dunking	finding	flying	frying
going	greeting	playing	reading
ringing	sending	washing

n	w	a	s	h	i	n	g	o
i	h	r	e	a	d	i	n	g
g	o	i	n	g	u	n	f	r
f	i	n	d	i	n	g	l	e
r	n	g	i	s	k	o	y	e
y	a	i	n	p	i	r	i	t
i	m	n	g	e	n	i	n	i
n	e	g	i	d	g	t	g	n
g	n	p	l	a	y	i	n	g

Hooked on First Grade *Spelling Super Workbook*

Yesterday or Today?

Some of these pictures show what Detective Dog did yesterday. Some of them show what he is doing today. Look at the pictures. Write the word that completes each sentence.

ducking feeding looked packed playing walked

Yesterday

Detective Dog _____ to the bank.

He _____ at some letters.

He _____ his bag.

Today

Detective Dog is _____ the ducks.

He is _____ some music.

He is _____ under the net.

244

ing or ed?

Write "ing" or "ed" to complete each sentence. Then draw a line to match each sentence to the correct picture.

The dog is bark_____ .

Cat pick_____ some apples.

The rat paint_____ a picture.

The bear is eat_____ corn.

The fish is sleep_____ .

Mad Dog finish_____ the race.

245

What Happened Lately?

Adding "ly" can make a word describe how something happens.

Change each word by adding "ly." Then write a sentence using one of the "ly" words.

late

late___

soft

soft___

kind

kind___

fair

fair___

sweet

sweet___

quiet

quiet___

_____

_____

Hooked on First Grade *Spelling Super Workbook*

How's It Done?

Write "ly" at the end of each word. Then write the new "ly" word to complete the sentence.

slow __ __

The snail moves _____ .

quick __ __

Mad Dog runs _____ to catch butterflies.

loud __ __

The Ratini Brother bangs _____ on his drum.

wild __ __

Mad Dog rides _____ on his skateboard.

sad __ __

Cat sits _____ on the bench.

247

What's Missing?

Write the word that completes each sentence.

Use the word box to help you.

| badly | calmly | proudly | wildly |

Cat _____ shows his painting.

Mad Dog plays _____ in the mud.

Mad Dog sings so _____ that his friends cannot listen.

Mad Dog rests _____ in bed.

Hooked on First Grade *Spelling Super Workbook*

Hit It!

Help Cat hit a home run.

Color the balls that describe how Cat could hit the ball.

shy

strongly

quickly

sweet

nicely

cool

softly

rich

swiftly

bravely

249

Say and Spell It!

Toss a coin onto the game board on the next page.

If it lands on a red star, add that ending to a word from a red box.

If the coin lands on a yellow star, add that ending to a word from a yellow box.

If it lands on a blue star, add that ending to a word from a blue box.

Say and spell each word out loud.

Use each word only once.

Write the words on the lines on the next page.

box	buzz	kick

go	play	start

talk	wait	sail

250

_____ _____

_____ _____

_____ _____

Hooked on First Grade *Spelling Super Workbook*

Word Hunt

Look at a page from your favorite book.

Are there any words that end with "er"?

Are there any words that end with "ed"?

Are there any words that end with "ing"?

Are there any words that end with "ly"?

Make a list of words you find with each ending.

Note to Parents
Talk with your child about how each ending changes the meaning of the base word. Have your child make up a story using some of the "er," "ed," "ing," and "ly" words that he found in his favorite book.

Silly Sentences

Read one of the tongue twisters below.

Say it fast three times.

Then try the other silly sentences!

The sleeping singer sadly shared seashells.

The bathing boxer had badly bruised bones.

The painting pirate picked partly painted pickle pictures.

The watching waiter wisely wished on Wednesday.

253

Answer Key

PAGE 194

chin; child; chess
chair; chest; chick

PAGE 195

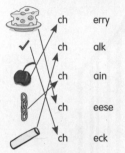

ch erry
ch alk
ch ain
ch eese
ch eck

PAGE 196

shell; shirt
ship; shoe

PAGE 197

PAGE 198

ship; chalk; shovel
check; chain; shoe

PAGE 199

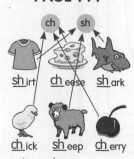

sh irt; ch eese; sh ark
ch ick; sh eep; ch erry

PAGE 200

thin; thick
think; thump

PAGE 201

m	t	h	a	t	i	y
e	t	s	t	h	e	n
t	h	e	r	e	s	a
h	i	h	a	y	i	h
y	s	m	r	s	r	x

PAGE 202

thumb; shark; think;
shell; ship; thump

PAGE 203

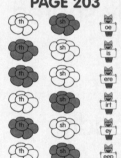

th / sh / oe
th / sh / is
th / sh / ere
th / sh / irt
th / sh / ey
th / sh / eep

PAGE 204

thumb; chain
thimble; chin
thorn; cherry

PAGE 205

cheese; they; chair;
this; check; there

PAGE 210

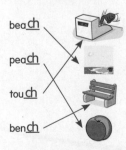

bea ch
pea ch
tou ch
ben ch

PAGE 211

which; beach;
much; rich

PAGE 212

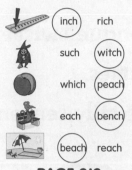

inch   rich
such   witch
which   peach
each   bench
beach   reach

PAGE 213

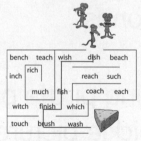

s	u	h	t	r	e
a	w	c	o	i	w
h	o	s	u	c	h
r	e	a	c	h	i
m	u	c	h	a	c
e	s	h	i	r	h

PAGE 214

leash; fish
dish; brush
wish; wash

PAGE 215

bench	teach	wish	dish	beach
inch	rich			
	much	fish	reach	such
witch	finish	which	coach	each
touch	brush	wash		

PAGE 216

wish; fish
brush; wash; dish

PAGE 217

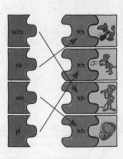

li / di sh
wa / we sh
bru / bre sh
lou / lea sh

PAGE 218

path; bath; mouth
moth; math; tooth

PAGE 219

su; mo; fa; co; wi; ba; ma; th; ne

PAGE 220

with; both
path; moth

PAGE 221

Across:
1. tooth
2. mouth
3. math

Down:
4. path
5. south
6. moth

PAGE 222

wa tch
pa tch
wi tch
sti tch
ske tch

PAGE 223

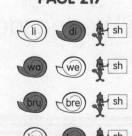

scra tch
ca tch
wa tch
pi tch

254

PAGE 224

PAGE 225

watch; stitch
sketch; patch

PAGE 226

pitch; touch
beach; catch
coach; switch

PAGE 227

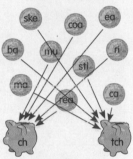

PAGE 232

boxer; pitcher
camper; catcher
painter; washer

PAGE 233

singer; camper
batter; painter

PAGE 234

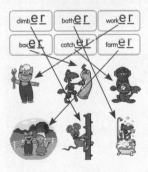

PAGE 235

mother; father;
brother; sister

PAGE 236

sailed; fished; cooked;
spilled; walked;
painted; washed;
finished

PAGE 237

looked; packed
licked; played

PAGE 238

painted
fished
camped
rested
walked
washed

PAGE 239

PAGE 240

sleeping; reading
yawning; packing
looking; thinking

PAGE 241

flying; standing
holding; drinking

PAGE 242

sailing; resting;
catching
boxing; splashing;
painting

PAGE 243

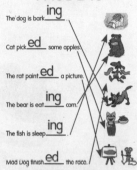

PAGE 244

walked; looked;
packed
feeding; playing;
ducking

PAGE 245

The dog is bark **ing**

Cat pick **ed** some apples

The rat paint **ed** a picture.

The bear is eat **ing** corn.

The fish is sleep **ing**

Mad Dog finish **ed** the race.

PAGE 246

lately; softly
kindly; fairly
sweetly; quietly

PAGE 247

slowly; quickly
loudly; wildly; sadly

PAGE 248

proudly; wildly
badly; calmly

PAGE 249

255

Hooked on First Grade *Spelling Super Workbook*

I did it!

Congratulations!

_____

- - - - - - - - - - - - - - - - - -

_____

has successfully completed this chapter.

1st Grade

Hooked on Phonics®

Spelling

Chapter 5

Add an a

Write an "a" to complete each word.

Then say each word out loud.

Sometimes the "a" sounds like the a in "apple."

Other times the "a" sounds like the a in "ape."

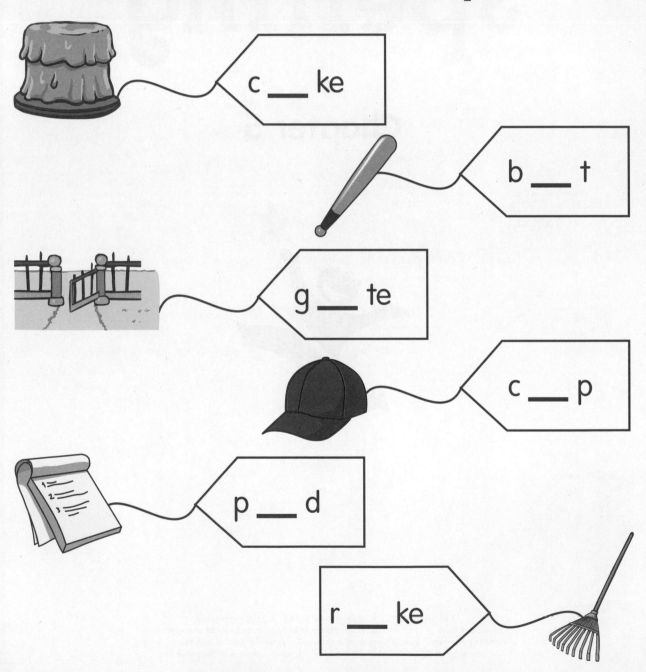

c __ ke

b __ t

g __ te

c __ p

p __ d

r __ ke

Match Game

Write an "a" to complete each word.
Draw a line from each picture to the matching word.

c __ t

w __ ve

m __ p

t __ pe

r __ g

c __ pe

259

Add an i

Write an "i" to complete each word.

Then say each word out loud.

Sometimes the "i" sounds like the i in "igloo."

Other times the "i" sounds like the i in "ice."

h __ de   b __ b   l __ d

b __ ke   t __ me   h __ t

Middle i

Unscramble the word that goes with each picture.
Write the word on the line.

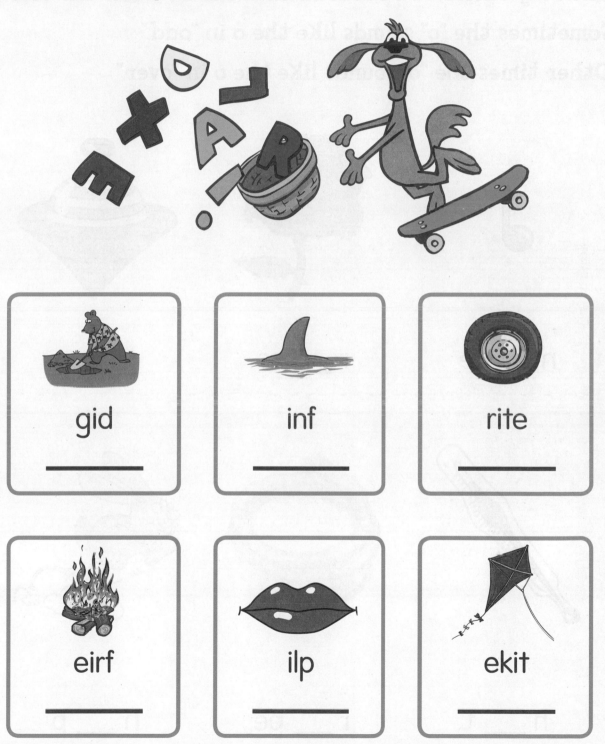

gid

_____

inf

_____

rite

_____

eirf

_____

ilp

_____

ekit

_____

261

Add an o

Write an "o" to complete each word.
Then say each word out loud.
Sometimes the "o" sounds like the o in "odd."
Other times the "o" sounds like the o in "over."

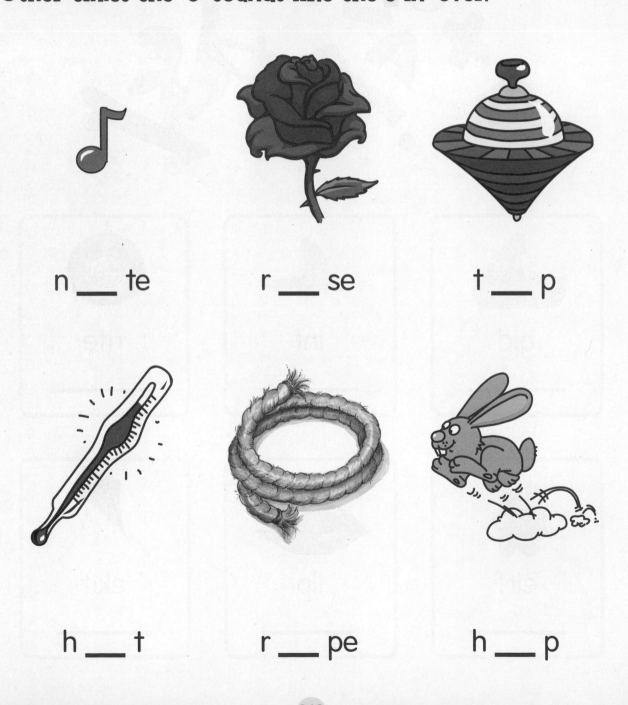

n__te   r__se   t__p

h__t   r__pe   h__p

Name Game

I did it!

Draw a line from each picture to the letters that complete the word.

b   ome

c   op

h   ob

m   ot

n   one

p   ose

e or u?

Write an "e" or a "u" to complete each word. Then say each word out loud. Sometimes "e" sounds like the e in "seat." Other times "e" sounds like the e in "red." Sometimes "u" sounds like the u in "blue." Other times "u" sounds like the u in "bug."

g __ m   n __ t   h __ t

m __ le   h __ n   b __ e

Word Hunt

Circle each word you find in the puzzle.
Look across and down.

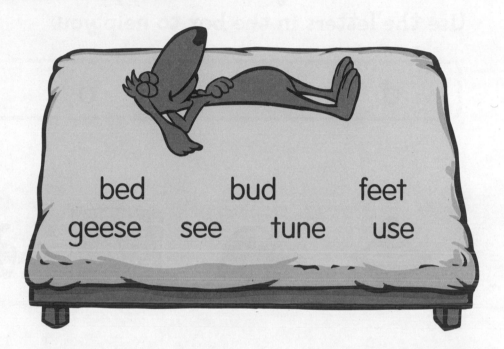

bed   bud   feet
geese   see   tune   use

g	e	e	s	e
t	b	e	d	f
u	u	s	e	e
n	d	a	d	e
e	a	r	m	t

Hooked on First Grade *Spelling Super Workbook*

Spell It Out!

Look at each picture.

Write the missing letter to complete each word.
Use the letters in the box to help you.

a	e	i	o	u

t__p   w__ve   m__p   b__ke

r__se   c__be   n__t   p__n

Write It Out!

Say the name of each thing out loud.

Write the word on the line. Use the words in the box to help you.

bed	bib	cake	gas
mop	cup	nose	tire

_____ _____ _____ _____

_____ _____ _____ _____

Hooked on First Grade *Spelling Super Workbook*

Add an a

Write an "a" to complete each word.

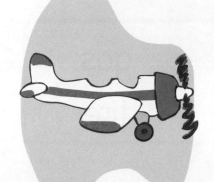

pl __ ne   sn __ ke   c __ pe

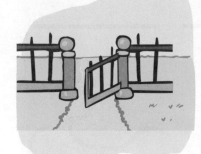

g __ te   sc __ le   c __ ve

What's Missing?

Write the words that complete each sentence.
Use the words in the box to help you.

lake	make	plane	race

Cat will _____ a wish
on his birthday.

Cat and Mad Dog
fly a _____ .

Mad Dog catches a fish
in the _____ .

Mad Dog wins the
_____ .

269

Add an i

Write an "i" to complete each word.

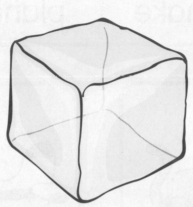

k __ te

__ ce

w __ pe

h __ de

h __ ke

l __ me

Name Game

Draw a line from each picture to the letters that complete each word.

	b		ire
	d		ite
	f		ine
	h		ike
	k		ive
	p		ime

Add an o

Write an "o" to complete each word.

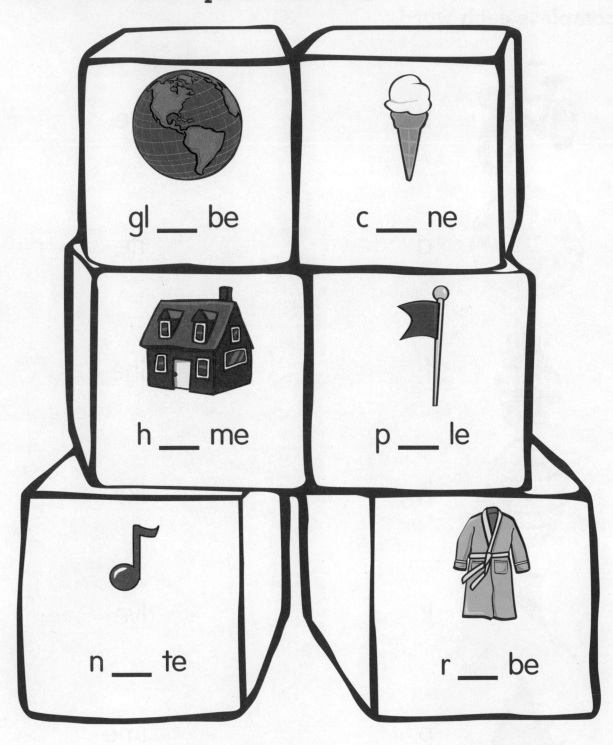

gl __ be

c __ ne

h __ me

p __ le

n __ te

r __ be

Hooked on First Grade *Spelling Super Workbook*

Oh No!

Unscramble the word that goes with each picture. Write the word on the line.

enob

_____

seon

_____

soer

_____

broe

_____

peor

_____

heonp

_____

273

e or u?

Write an "e" or a "u" to complete each word.

monk__y

m__le

r__ler

k__y

To the Beach

I did it!

Help Cat get to the beach.

Write an "e" or a "u" to complete each word.

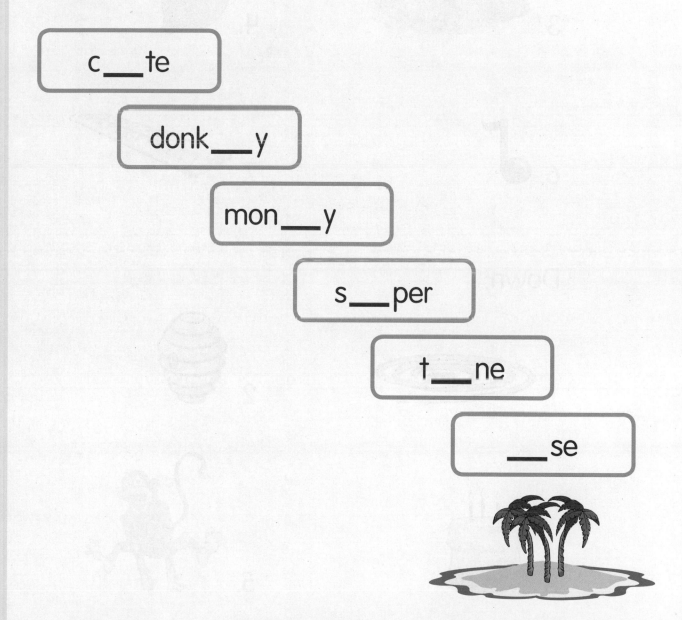

c___te

donk___y

mon___y

s___per

t___ne

___se

Hooked on First Grade *Spelling Super Workbook*

Crazy Crossword

Use the pictures as clues to fill in the crossword puzzle on the next page.

Across:

3.

4.

6.

7.

Down:

1.

2.

3.

5.

276

Hooked on First Grade *Spelling Super Workbook*

Picture This!

This is a game for two or more players.

You will need:

one coin

How to play:

1. The first player flips the coin. If it lands on heads, the first player draws a picture of something from the Heads box on the next page. If it lands on tails, he draws a picture of something from the Tails box on the next page. The other players then guess what the word is.

2. The next player flips the coin. He draws a picture of a different word from the Heads or Tails box.

3. The players take turns until all of the words have been drawn.

Heads

ape	cage	plane
kite	nose	rope

Tails

cake	wave	bike
lake	hose	flute

Note to Parents
You can add extra words for players to draw. The new words should also be nouns.

Add ai or ay

Write "ai" or "ay" to complete each word.

h ___

r ___ n

spr ___

s ___ lboat

cr ___ on

m ___ lbox

Pick Flowers

I did it!

Help Cat pick the flowers.

Color the flower that completes each word.

 d    ai    ay

 pl    ay    ai

 st    ai    ay

 tr    ail    ayl

 w    ayt    ait

    Hooked on First Grade *Spelling Super Workbook*

Word Hunt

Circle each word you find in the puzzle.
Look across and down.

clay	hay	paint	rain
sail	say		trail

x	o	r	w	p
y	k	a	c	a
s	a	i	l	i
a	y	n	a	n
y	h	a	y	t
t	r	a	i	l

282

Circle or X?

Look at each picture. How is it spelled? Circle each thing that is spelled with the letters "ai." Put an X on things that are spelled with the letters "ay."

 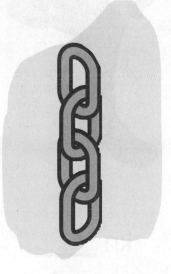 

283

Add ee or ea

Write "ee" or "ea" to complete each word.

l ___ f

ch ___ se

b ___ ch

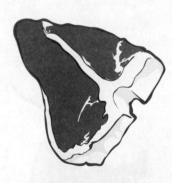

b ___

kn ___

m ___ t

Which Word?

Circle the word in each pair that is spelled correctly.

feal	feel
heat	heet
frea	free
reach	reech
meal	meel
teath	teeth

285

ee or ea?

Help Mad Dog get from here to there.

Write "ee" or "ea" to complete each word.

here

ch _____ k

cl _____ n

gr _____ n

l _____ p

qu _____ n

tr _____ t

there

Puzzle Time

I did it!

Use the picture clues and the word box to fill in the puzzle.

ear	peach	seal	sheep	tree

Across: 2.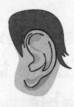

3.

Down: 1.

3.

4.

287

Mix and Match

This is a game for two players.

You will need:
index cards

How to play:

1. Write each word you see on the next page onto two different index cards. Mix up the cards and place them face down on a table.

2. The first player turns over two cards.

3. If the cards show the same word, it's a match! The player spells the word out loud and Keeps the cards.

4. If the words are not the same, the player turns both cards face down again and it becomes the next player's turn.

5. Keep taking turns until all of the matches have been made. The player with the most cards wins.

288

sail	mail
away	stay
peach	beach
feet	meet

Hooked on First Grade *Spelling Super Workbook*

oa or ow?

Write "oa" or "ow" to complete each word.

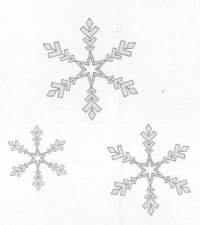

b ___ t   sn ___   pill ___

b ___ l   c ___ t   g ___ t

oa or ow?

Help Cat get to Grandma's farm.

Write "ow" or "oa" to complete each word.

c _____ t

fl _____

cr _____

r _____ d

sl _____

s _____ p

291

Which Word?

Don't burst Mad Dog's bubble. Circle the word that is spelled correctly in each pair.

toast   toest

snoe   snow

goes   goas

elbow   elboe

coech   coach

toa   toe

Word Hunt

Circle each word you find in the puzzle.
Look across and down.

coast	glow	goes
oak	show	toe

c	g	o	e	s
o	l	k	q	h
a	o	a	k	o
s	w	p	h	w
t	o	e	i	o

293

oa, ow, or oe?

Write the letters that complete each word.

Then say each word aloud.

Sometimes the o sound is spelled "oa" as in "oak."

Sometimes the o sound is spelled "ow" as in "yellow."

Sometimes the o sound is spelled "oe" as in "Joe."

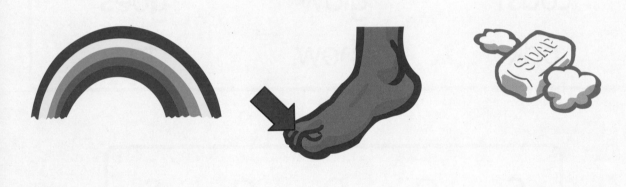

rainb ___ ___   t ___ ___ ___   s ___ ___ ___ p

wind ___ ___ ___   r ___ ___ ___ d   h ___ ___ ___

What's Missing?

Write the word that completes each sentence. Use the word box to help you.

| blows | boat | soap | tiptoe |

Mad Dog _____

a bubble.

Mad Dog washes

with _____.

Mad Dog walks

on _____.

Mad Dog steers

a _____.

Hooked on First Grade *Spelling Super Workbook*

Circle or X?

Draw a circle around the things that are spelled with "oo."

Draw an X across the things that are spelled with a "u."

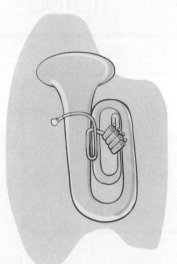

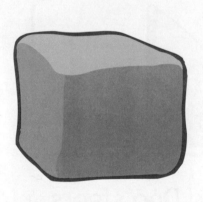

oo or u?

Draw a line from each picture to the letter or letters that complete the word. Write the letter or letters on the lines.

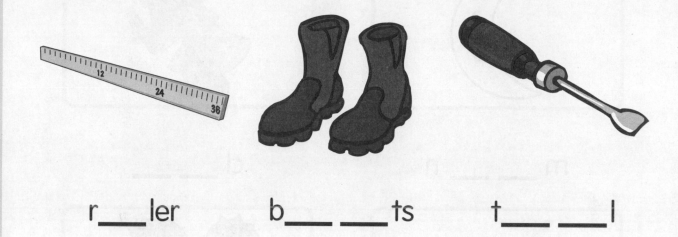

r___ler   b___ ___ts   t___ ___l

oo   u

t___be   m___sic   ball___ ___n

297

oo or ue?

Write "oo" or "ue" to complete each word.

m __ __ n

cl __ __

br __ __ m

bl __ __ berries

sp __ __ n

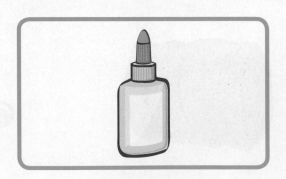

gl __ __

Which Bone?

Help Mad Dog make some words.
Color the bone that completes each word.

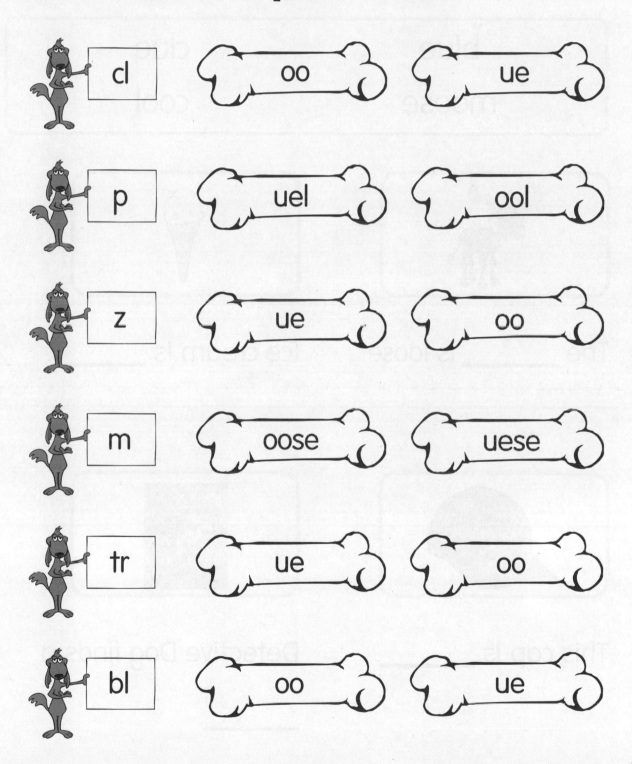

cl	oo	ue
p	uel	ool
z	ue	oo
m	oose	uese
tr	ue	oo
bl	oo	ue

299

What's Missing?

Write the words that complete each sentence. Use the word box to help you.

blue	clue
moose	cool

The _____ is loose.

Ice cream is _____.

This cap is _____.

Detective Dog finds a _____.

Word Hunt

Circle each word you find
in the puzzle.

Look across and down.

blue	boom	due	fuel
spoon		too	true

t	r	u	e	b
o	b	z	f	o
o	l	h	u	o
d	u	e	e	m
a	e	t	l	r
s	p	o	o	n

301

Middle oo

Write "oo" to complete each word. Then draw a line from each word to its matching picture.

b __ __ k

m __ __ n

w __ __ d

c __ __ kie

f __ __ d

br __ __ m

Middle oo

Unscramble the word that goes with each picture. Write the word on the line.

Then say each word out loud.

Sometimes the letters "oo" sound like the "oo" in "book."

Other times the letters "oo" sound like the "oo" in "room."

 koorb

_____

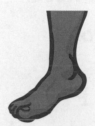 tofo

_____

 ozo

_____

 foro

_____

 choosl

_____

303

Day at the Beach

Help Detective Dog get to the beach.

This is a game for two players.

You will need:

three coins

How to play:

1. Each player takes a coin to use as a playing piece.

2. The first player flips the third coin. If the coin lands on tails, the player moves one space. If the coin lands on heads, the player moves two spaces.

3. Then the player acts out the sentence on the space.

4. Take turns until both players get to the beach.

START

Walk on tiptoe.

Eat a bowl of oatmeal.

Tie a bow.

Sail a boat.

Cook some food.

Plant a tree.

Read a book.

Go back one space.

Crawl through a tube.

Blow up a balloon.

FINISH

A Spelling Story

This is a game for two or more players.

Each player chooses five words from the list on the next page.

Write a story using the five words.

Then take turns reading the stories out loud.

Note to Parents
The words on the list can be challenging for children to spell because they can't decode the spelling just by sounding out the words. Sometimes different letter combinations make the same sound, and sometimes the same letter combinations make different sounds!

This is a game for two players.

You will need:
index cards

How to play:

1. Copy each word from the list below onto an index card.

2. Shuffle the cards. Then deal them so that each player has nine cards.

3. The first player reads the word on one of his cards out loud.

4. The other player spells the the word. If the player spells the word correctly, he gets to keep the card.

5. Keep taking turns until you have spelled all of the words. The player with the most cards wins.

baboon	food
balloon	music
blueberries	pillow
boots	slow
clue	toast
cookie	toe
door	soap
elbow	tube
float	zoo

Hooked on First Grade *Spelling Super Workbook*

More than One

Sometimes vowels sound exactly like their letter. They are called long vowels.

The "a" in ape is a long vowel. It sounds like a.

The "u" in tune is a long vowel too. It sounds like u.

Say the name of each thing out loud. Write the name on the line. Use the words in the box to help you.

bees	bones	cubes
keys	tigers	snakes

The Plural Path

Circle all the words that have long vowel sounds. Then help Mad Dog get to the Finish by drawing a path through the circled words that are plural.

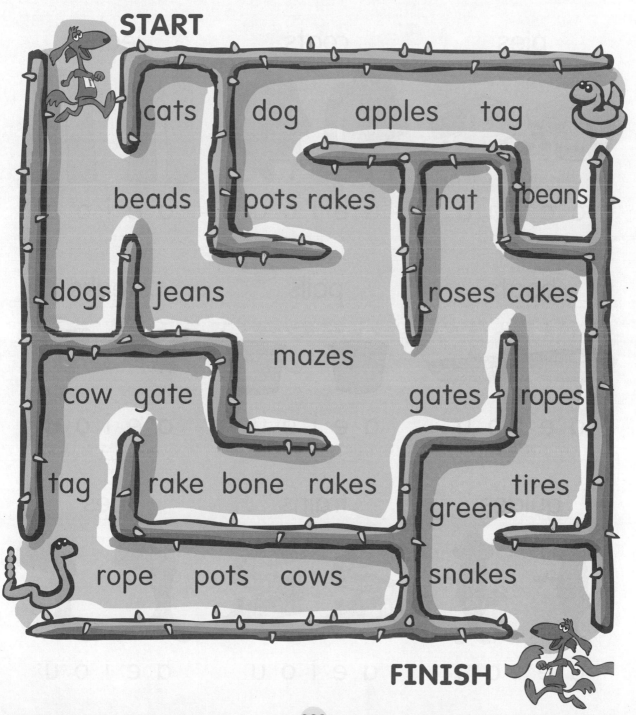

START

cats   dog   apples   tag

beads   pots rakes   hat   beans

dogs   jeans   roses cakes

mazes

cow   gate   gates   ropes

tag   rake   bone   rakes   tires
greens

rope   pots   cows   snakes

FINISH

Hooked on First Grade *Spelling Super Workbook*

Two Letters, One Sound

Sometimes when two vowels are next to each other, only one vowel makes a sound.

Say each word out loud. Then circle the vowel that is heard. Draw an X over the vowel that is not heard.

pies

a e i o u

coats

a e i o u

jeans

a e i o u

boats

a e i o u

pails

a e i o u

steaks

a e i o u

guides

a e i o u

trains

a e i o u

toes

a e i o u

310

Scrambled Words

Unscramble the word that goes with each picture.
Write the word on the line.

wsbo

_____

odsra

_____

tsase

_____

hewles

_____

atsipn

_____

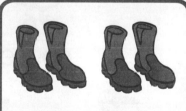
otsob

_____

311

Add ee

Write "ee" to make these words plural.

foot

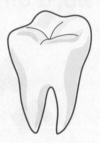

tooth

f __ __ t

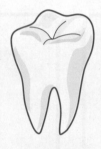 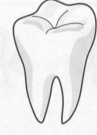

t __ __ th

goose

sheep

g __ __ se

sh __ __ p

312

Word Hunt

I did it!

Circle each word you find in the puzzle.
Look across and down.

feet	geese	knives
mice	teeth	wolves

f	e	e	t	g	w
m	i	c	e	g	o
i	a	t	e	e	l
l	n	i	t	e	v
k	t	n	h	s	e
k	n	i	v	e	s

Hooked on First Grade *Spelling Super Workbook*

Plural Puzzle

Use the picture clues to fill in the crossword puzzle on the next page.

Across:

2.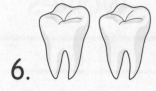

5.

6.

7.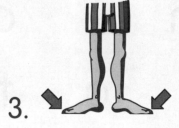

8.

Down:

1.

3.

4.

5.

Searching for Sounds

Put a blanket on the ground outdoors or in a room in your house.

Sit on the blanket and look around.

Name the things that you see.

Which things have long vowel sounds?
(Hint: A long vowel sounds exactly like its letter.)

Make a list of all the things you see that have long vowel sounds.

Note to Parents
This version of I Spy helps children discriminate between long and short vowel sounds. As your child identifies words with long vowel sounds, remind him that long vowel sounds are spelled in different ways.

When you're cleaning up, say the names of the things you put away.

Which things are spelled with long vowel sounds? Make a list of all the words with long vowel sounds.

Hooked on First Grade *Spelling Super Workbook*

Answer Key

PAGE 258

cake; bat; gate; cap; pad; rake

PAGE 259

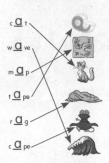

c <u>a</u> t
w <u>a</u> ve
m <u>a</u> p
t <u>a</u> pe
r <u>a</u> g
c <u>a</u> pe

PAGE 260

hide; bib; lid
bike; time; hit

PAGE 261

dig; fin; tire
fire; lip; kite

PAGE 262

note; rose; top
hot; rope; hop

PAGE 263

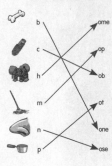

b — ome
c — op
h — ob
m — ot
n — one
p — ose

PAGE 264

gum; net; hut
mule; hen;
bee

PAGE 265

g e e s e
t b e d f
u n u s e e
n d a d e
e a r m t

PAGE 266

top; wave; map
bike; rose; cube
net; pin

PAGE 267

cake; mop; gas
bed; cup; nose
tire; bib

PAGE 268

plane; snake; cape
gate; scale; cave

PAGE 269

make; plane
lake; race

PAGE 270

kite; ice; wipe
hide; hike; lime

PAGE 271

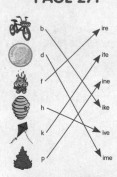

b — ire
d — ite
f — ine
h — ike
k — ive
p — ime

PAGE 272

globe; cone; home
pole; note; robe

PAGE 273

bone; nose; rose
robe; rope; phone

PAGE 274

monkey; mule
ruler; key

PAGE 275

cute; donkey
money; super
tune; use

PAGE 277

Across:
   3. cave
   4. lime
   6. note
   7. ruler
Down:
   1. hose
   2. hive
   3. cake
   5. monkey

PAGE 280

hay; rain; spray
sailboat; crayon
mailbox

PAGE 281

day
play
stay
trail
wait

PAGE 282

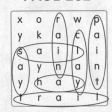

x o r w p
y k a c a
s a i l i
a y n a n
y h a y t
t r a i l

PAGE 283

PAGE 284

leaf; cheese
beach; bee
knee; meat

PAGE 285

feal — feel
heat — heet
frea — free
reach — reech
meal — meel
teath — teeth

PAGE 286

cheek; clean; green
leap; queen; treat

PAGE 287

Across:
   2. ear
   3. sheep
Down:
   1. tree
   3. seal
   4. peach

PAGE 290

boat; snow; pillow
bowl; coat; goat

PAGE 291

coat; flow; crow
road; slow; soap

318

PAGE 292

toast | toest
snoe | snow
goes | goas
elbow | elboe
coech | coach
toa | toe

PAGE 293

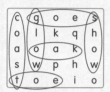

PAGE 294

rainbow; toe
soap; window
road; hoe

PAGE 295

blows; soap
tiptoe; boat

PAGE 296

PAGE 297

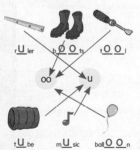

r__U__ler   b__OO__ts   t__OO__l

oo → u

t__U__be   m__U__sic   ball__OO__n

PAGE 298

moon; clue
broom; blueberries
spoon; glue

PAGE 299

clue
pool
zoo
moose
true
blue

PAGE 300

moose; cool
blue; clue

PAGE 301

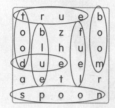

PAGE 302

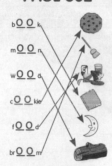

b__OO__k
m__OO__n
w__OO__d
c__OO__kie
f__OO__d
br__OO__m

PAGE 303

brook; foot
zoo; roof
school

PAGE 308

bees; tigers
snakes; keys
cubes; bones

PAGE 309

PAGE 310

pies   coats   jeans
boats   pails   steaks
guides trains   toes

PAGE 311

bows; roads
seats; wheels
paints; boots

PAGE 312

feet; teeth
geese; sheep

PAGE 313

PAGE 315

Across.
2. mice
5. bees
6. teeth
7. pies
8. seals

Down:
1. kisses
3. feet
4. geese
5. bones

319

I did it!

Congratulations!

_____

— — — — — — — — — — — — — — — — —

_____

has successfully completed this chapter.